WONDERS OF THE ANIMAL WORLD

WALT DISNEY

WONDERS
OF THE ANIMAL
WORLD

Text by Vezio Melegari

 GOLDEN PRESS • NEW YORK

LIBRARY OF CONGRESS CATALOG CARD NUMBER 64-24908

© COPYRIGHT 1964, 1963 BY WALT DISNEY PRODUCTIONS

ALL RIGHTS RESERVED, INCLUDING THE RIGHT OF REPRODUCTION

IN WHOLE OR IN PART IN ANY FORM.

PRODUCED IN THE UNITED STATES OF AMERICA

BY WESTERN PUBLISHING COMPANY, INC.

SECOND PRINTING, 1968

Since we started the True-Life Adventure film series, our files have been enriched with marvelous pictures of animals. All the things that the lens collects in nature lead us to reflect; they are causes for joy and admiration; they invite us to enjoy the world around us. But, in nature, there are certain creatures that represent the wonderful.

What we have attempted to bring together in these pages are some of the wonderful and strange creatures that inhabit our earth. They are found in all parts of the globe from Tasmania to the Galapagos, from Africa to South America. We hope that you will enjoy meeting these unique members of the animal world.

WALT DISNEY

CONTENTS

STRANGE ONES

There is always a cause for what exists in nature, no matter how strange it may seem to us. When we fail to find that cause, we have failed to understand the truth which underlies the existence of that which we are observing. To some this is the greatest beauty of the natural world: that form and function complement each other so perfectly.

However, there are animals and forms on the face of the earth today that we may properly describe as strange. But by this we mean only strange to our expectations of the way things should be, which is based in general on the way we find most things are. The platypus, for example, contradicts our expectations by combining features of both reptiles and mammals: it lays eggs and suckles its young. Yet, when we consider that the platypus evolved on a continent largely isolated from the rest of the natural world, it is not strange that it possesses features in combinations that do not exist elsewhere.

THE PLATYPUS

LONDON, 1798—One day a tall sunburnt man, swaying a little in his walk as sailors do, waited patiently to see a famous professor. Luckily, he did not have to wait long. The professor, one of the most important naturalists of England, appeared and invited him into his office. The sailor, a little ill at ease, hat in hand and a package under his right arm, looked around. He saw stuffed animals placed here and there, a large number of bottles ranged on the shelves, and a long white marble table toward which he went at a sign from the professor. He stammered a few words and put the package down on the cold marble. He opened it unhurriedly. And there "it" was, between the two men. It was an unknown dead animal, a sort of big mole with rumpled fur and an odd beak, like a duck. The professor took up a magnifying glass and the sailor started

The most common trees found in Australia are the eucalyptus, or gum trees. There are more than five hundred species of them on this continent.

to talk. He said that he had come from a far place, a new continent, Australia. Yes, that animal had been captured at Hawkesbury, in New South Wales. It lived there with others like it, by a stream. The natives say that the female lays eggs and that the male has spurs on his hind legs that can cause serious wounds because they inject a poisonous liquid.

The professor looked at the sailor, went back to the animal, and then rendered his decision: Humbug!

This was a time of sensational discoveries and hoaxes. The newspapers printed stories about sailors cheated by Chinese embalmers who sold them fabricated mummies, at fabulous prices. Some of the sailors had even brought back "mermaids" manufactured from the cadavers of monkeys, to which fishtails had been skillfully sewn. This duck-billed creature must be the work of a forger. Such was the opinion given, with great calm, by Mr. George Shaw, eminent professor of the British Museum. Since the sailor insisted, the professor was kind enough to promise him to make a more detailed examination. He would consult a learned colleague. If the sailor could possibly arrange to come back a few days later, he would get his answer.

And the sailor came back, to be told that his animal had gone off to Göttingen for definitive study by one of the greatest scientific authorities of the time, Johann Friedrich Blumenbach. He was a shining light of medicine and zoology, and one of the fathers

The platypus (left) is one of the curiosities of the animal world, hatched from an egg like a snake or a bird, but nursed on milk like a mammal. Once hunted for its furry pelt, it is now protected in Australia, the only country where it is found.

of modern anthropology. And Blumenbach confirmed what Shaw had come around to suspecting: the remains were those of a genuine animal. That is how, at the end of the eighteenth century, the existence of the platypus, or ornithorhynchus, was discovered—the egg-laying mammal, which can give fatal wounds with the poisonous spurs of its hind legs. Actually, it probably only kills its own kind, and then only in battles among males that humans have imagined but that no one has reported seeing.

In 1809 the French scientist Lamarck classified the platypus and the other animals of the same order in a class belonging to neither the mammals nor the reptiles.

The platypus continues to live its mysterious life and tries to avoid man. And man, the animal's great enemy who waged an unrelenting war upon it to get its silky fur, is now protecting it. At least most people in Australia are attempting to prevent its extinction.

The platypus makes its burrow among the roots of trees, in skillfully concealed grottoes with several entrances. But the female is not satisfied with this communal dwelling; she requires another for herself when it is time for her to lay her eggs, in order to protect her brood. This nest is set in the bank above the level of a lake or river, and is carpeted with wet eucalyptus leaves. When everything is ready, the female closes all the entrances of her retreat and, in the darkness, lays two or three eggs no bigger than those of a pigeon.

When the incubation period is over, the young one about to be hatched uses its egg-tooth, a hard excrescence on the maxillary bone, to split the shell. Birds usually use the egg-tooth on their upper beaks for that purpose, but the platypus has no beak at birth. The beak forms later, when the young platypus stops feeding on its mother's milk, and when it must learn to dive under the water in search of small crabs, worms and mollusks. During these dives it closes its eyes and ears, and seeks food with its sensitive beak.

This animal is very much affected by noise. It is said that platypuses have been killed by loud noises. One of them, being sent to Winston Churchill as a gift, died on board ship just outside of Liverpool. It was during the Second World War, and the sea lanes were infested by German submarines. A depth bomb exploded nearby, causing the walls of the ship to vibrate. The platypus was mortally hurt; an hour later it was dead.

15

From just this much of it, we might take the animal pictured on the left to be a deer. In fact it is a young kangaroo, another of the animal curiosities that are found naturally today only in Australia and Tasmania.

THE KANGAROOS

THE first European to see kangaroos was the Dutch seaman Pelsart, in 1629. His ship was wrecked on an Australian reef; he got to land exhausted and lay down to rest in the grass. Suddenly he saw a fleeing herd of animals with heads like dogs, making huge leaps. He had just time to see that they had very small front legs, enormous hind legs and long muscular tails.

When he finally got back to Europe, he described these strange creatures. Other adventurers after him confirmed his report. And so the existence of these Australian animals became known in Europe. But their name came from the English Captain James Cook, the famous explorer who wrote in his journal in 1770, in Australia: "(This animal) has the light color of a mouse, the build of a greyhound and quite the appearance of that dog, with a long tail, which he carries in the same manner . . . except for his way of walking or running, which is like the leaping of a hare or a deer." He asked native Australians the name of this surprising beast. He asked them in English, of course, and the aborigines answered in their language, "Can ga ru," meaning (more or less) "I don't understand." Cook took this as being an answer to his question, and the name kangaroo has been used ever since.

The natives' name for the true kangaroo is walaru or wallaroo and they have retained it. These are the large kangaroos. Those that Cook had seen were wallabies, the smaller kangaroos. But whether large or small, and there are a number of very different species,

16

These kangaroos seem to be eating peacefully now, but at the first threat of danger they will be off, bounding away at nearly thirty miles an hour.

all of the animals that we call kangaroos belong to the family of marsupials. (Most marsupials, except the opossums, are found only in the southern hemisphere.)

The name marsupial comes from the Latin word for "pouch," and was given these animals because in almost all, the females have an abdominal pouch in which their young pass the first months of their life. Even after they have started to come out and look for their own food, they still use their mother's pouch as a shelter from danger.

This pouch contains the teats at which the young feed for several months. When the little kangaroos are born, the mother licks a path on the hairs of her abdomen up to the pouch, which they can then find with ease. The young kangaroos, or joeys, continue using their mother's pouch until they outgrow it. The female usually gives birth to one, but sometimes two, young.

It is thought by some scientists that kangaroos lived in trees originally. It is not known how or why they came down to the

ground to live. However, one group, the tree kangaroos, have returned to life in the trees, sleeping and feeding there.

Kangaroos, unlike many other animals, have no lairs or burrows. They get along without any shelter, roaming freely and leaping with those tremendous leaps that so impressed the first explorers of Australia. These broad jumps, which may measure as much as twenty feet, give them remarkable speed, up to twenty-five miles an hour. They rest on their powerful hind legs, and use their tails for additional support. An adult great gray kangaroo male may measure almost seven feet from the tip of his nose to the tip of his tail, and can weigh over two hundred pounds.

Although it is hard to keep the big kangaroo in captivity, there are many in zoos throughout the world. They have even been bred in some zoos.

The tree kangaroos are not over three feet in length. Unlike the terrestrial kangaroos, their front and hind legs are almost equal in size. Their big strong tails are used as rudders when they jump to the ground from the trees in which they live, sometimes from a height of sixty or seventy feet.

The best-known wallabies, because they are the most apt to be seen in captivity, are probably the rock wallabies. They vary in size; there are several species. The soles of their hind paws are protected by a pad that keeps them from slipping. In Australia they can be seen in rocky areas running and leaping, searching for the vegetation they feed on, such as leaves, grass, roots, and bark. Nothing is more graceful than a wallaby's leap; even the smallest can make tremendous jumps.

Since foxes and dogs have been introduced into Australia, the smaller kangaroos

18

Accommodating is the word for the mother kangaroo, for a while. Until it outgrows the space, the young kangaroo, or joey, has a home in its mother's pouch, which it enters soon after birth. Usually kangaroos have just one young, or sometimes two.

have mortal enemies. They escape by jumping, and do not hesitate to jump into trees, using their front paws, like velvet-covered hands, to hold on to the branches.

All kangaroos are herbivorous; most of them eat leaves or grass. In order to get leaves, the tree kangaroos climb trees, bracing themselves with their tails. They may spend long hours during the day sleeping in the fork of a tree.

Rat kangaroos feed on grass and tubers and are sometimes a nuisance to farmers. They are about the size of rabbits. They use their long tails to carry grasses with which they build their nests. They are also preyed upon by the foxes which were brought to Australia by the early settlers.

THE COCK-OF-THE-ROCK

THE eastern cock-of-the-rock and the Peruvian cock-of-the-rock live in South America, and nest on rocks near rivers and brooks. They are splendid birds about a foot long, strong and solid looking, with brilliant plumage. The males are more imposing and colorful than the females and have a crest that goes like a fan from the top of their heads to the base of their beaks.

19

In Colombia and Peru the cocks-of-the-rock are flame-colored red with black wings; in Brazil and Guiana, they are a sumptuous orange-yellow. The female is smaller and has brown feathers. Despite this apparent drabness, she seems to inspire the male to heroic frenzies and exhibitions of acrobatics, dances and shows of color.

When the mating season arrives, the males pick out suitable forest clearings for their dance performances, beating their wings and hopping on the dancing grounds. Each show is carefully watched by the males awaiting their turn, by those who have finished, and by the females for whose benefit the show is being given. The vocal accompaniment is not like the usual singing of birds. It has been described as being like the rustling of branches, like laundry flapping in the wind, like the scraping of metal, like whistling or even like a carillon.

Cocks-of-the-rock are rare and many of their habits are unknown. Some fanciers raise them as pets, and they are shown in some zoos. In captivity, they eat fruits, and are particularly fond of grapes.

The cock-of-the-rock, found in the Guianas and northern Brazil, lives in the lower part of the tropical forest, building its nest of mud and twigs.

An Australian "sugar squirrel," or flying phalanger, which "flies" on a parachute-like membrane stretched between its hind- and fore-legs. The "sugar squirrel" is a marsupial and, like the kangaroo, carries its young in a pouch on its belly.

THE FLYING SQUIRRELS

SQUIRRELS are attractive animals, belonging to the Sciuridae family, which is so large that scientists have divided it into sub-families. In Greek the family name means "shade tail." Our common tree squirrels belong to the Sciuridae; the flying squirrels are classified as Petauristidae, a sub-family. Among its members are the common flying squirrel of North America and the rare *Eoglaucomys*, the Himalayan flying squirrels, which inhabit the mountains of Tibet.

All flying squirrels resemble each other sufficiently so that what is said about any one of them applies in general to all. Those of the United States and Canada are active at night. They collect nuts, fruits and grain, and store them in abandoned woodpecker holes. These are the graceful *Glaucomys*

sabrinus, with their big bright eyes. They are very hard to observe in their native habitat because they sleep during the day.

It is really not a misnomer to describe these squirrels as "flying": their leaps of up to one hundred feet from tree to tree are not leaps but glides. They are made possible by the thin hairy membrane that extends the length of each side of their body, between the front and hind legs. During the squirrel's glide this membrane acts like a parachute. With this equipment, the flying squirrel can glide from one tree to another. Its beautiful long tail, with long silky hair, is used as a rudder in the squirrel's gliding flight. According to some observers, the tail is used for steering; according to others it is used to regulate the squirrel's speed.

The flying squirrel of the Malacca Peninsula is also found in South China and Thailand; its local name is taguan.

The taguan is highly valued for its meat, and the natives spread nets between the trees at sundown to catch it. It is easily tamed and does well in captivity

Another flying squirrel, *Petaurillus hosei*, is tiny—eight inches in all, including body and tail—with an elegant white tuft at the

Although the "flying squirrel" does not fly but glides from tree to tree, its hundred-foot leaps, with flying membrane spread, certainly give it the appearance of flight.

end of its tail. This little squirrel lives in the trees of forests in Borneo and is active at night. It is trapped by men, not for its meat, but for its beautiful fur.

The "flying squirrels" of Australia are not really squirrels but phalangers. Like most of the other native animals of this continent, they are marsupials. The flying phalangers also glide rather than fly.

THE ECHIDNA

When people unfamiliar with the existence of the echidna hear a description of it and its behavior, based on anatomical and physiological facts, their typical reaction is: "Impossible! Inconceivable!"

Toward the end of the eighteenth century and the beginning of the nineteenth, when naturalists were beginning to exchange information about monotremes—platypuses and echidnas—they had endless discussions that provided the reading public with great entertainment.

Even today, when there is so much more information available about them, people are still amazed at these primitive mammals. They are thought to be survivals from times so ancient that they still retain some reptilian characteristics. They have been the subject of volumes of more or less well-founded guesses, hypotheses and heated arguments by scientists.

Australia, the last habitable continent to be discovered by Europeans, confounded explorers by its unexpected fauna. The echidna is a striking example.

The echidna measures sixteen to twenty inches from the tip of its beaked snout to its tiny tail hidden under a thicket of pointed bristles. Its long tongue is conical and retractable, like that of the tropical American anteater. It has no teeth, but there are small fleshy excrescences on its palate. Mixed in with its fur are dense hard spines. Most of the spines are set in among the fur, but some, up to an inch or two in length, very thick and pointed, stand upright. The animal also resembles the American anteater in that it hunts for its food at night. It escapes danger by digging a hole in the ground. It eats ants, opening anthills with its claws.

The female lays a single egg with a membranous shell like those of reptile eggs, and hatches it in a pouch on her abdomen. In its first days the newborn infant feeds on its mother's milk, which oozes out of a mam-

known in which this weapon has been used. The echidna seems to prefer an effective method of passive defense; it either rolls up into a ball, showing its spines to the enemy, or else it digs its way into the earth, disappearing rapidly. One captive echidna dug a two-foot deep hole in two minutes.

The echidna, or spiny anteater, is native to Australia and nearby Tasmania and New Guinea. A mammal, like its equally rare relative the platypus, it is hatched from an egg and nursed on its mother's milk.

mary surface on the inside of her pouch. This fact is what causes scientists to classify the echidna among the mammals, although some see resemblances to the reptiles, especially since the body temperature of echidnas varies greatly in response to the temperature of the air around them.

When the baby echidna's spines grow large enough to make the mother uncomfortable, she expels it from her pouch.

The male has a fleshy spur on its hind legs, like the male platypus. Few cases are

There are several kinds of echidnas found in Australia, Tasmania, and New Guinea. The one that lives on the island of Tasmania is larger than the Australian echidna and has longer hair. The echidna of New Guinea is about thirty inches long, the largest of all.

Before Australia was colonized, the aborigines hunted the echidnas both for their meat and for their strong spines, which were used to make arrows.

Today the echidna has become rare and is protected by law. It can be seen in zoos.

REMOTE ONES

Those who talk about the splendors or beauty of the world of nature frequently limit themselves to the plants and animals found on land. Actually only a relatively small portion of the earth is exposed above the surface of the encircling waters. In fact, the waters of our globe are as much a part of the natural world as the deepest forests, and the home of just as much that is curious and beautiful to see.

It is inconvenient to survey the watery kingdoms, however, and it is true still that half of the surface of the Moon has been more exactly charted than most of the seas and oceans of our earth. At all levels the waters and especially the waters of the oceans teem with life, from the giant to the microscopic in size. As yet we have only sampled the ocean surfaces, only discovered a small part of vast and various array of life that they contain.

CHAULIODUS SLOANI

FOR centuries man knew nothing of the sea below five fathoms deep. He thought that the vast abyss, dark and unapproachable, did not harbor any kind of life. Today man keeps learning more and more about the submarine world. Diving suits, bathyscaphes, sounding apparatus, electromagnetic waves and other inventions, and increasingly precise instruments, have enabled scientists to collect extremely valuable information about the life of the depths. Still, despite the increasing boldness of men and

the steady progress of science, most of the secrets under the sea are yet hidden from us. The expression "mysteries of the depths" continues to keep its value and significance.

Beyond two hundred feet deep, there is still a great deal left to discover. And beyond a thousand feet, where very little sunlight ever penetrates, there is much not yet accessible to our knowledge.

In the kingdom of darkness, dimly lit by the phantasmagoria of the photophores, life takes on a dramatic intenseness. Huge

Chauliodus sloani *is one of the more ferocious-looking denizens of the abyssal deep. But for all its sharp and fearful teeth, it is only eight inches long.*

The tree frog is an amphibian. It is born in water and it lays eggs and fertilizes them in water, but it spends most of its adult life on land.

mouths, sabre-like teeth, elastic and extensible bodies that can swallow prey bigger than the predator itself: such are the characteristics of abyssal fish, genuine monsters as compared to the fish of the surface waters. And yet their seeming monstrosity is only due to the requirements of adaptation to the environment.

Among the representatives of the abyssal fauna, special mention should be made of *Chauliodus sloani*, first discovered two hundred years ago, quite accidentally. The discoverer was Sir Hans Sloane, an English physician and botanist of the eighteenth century.

"And here, ladies and gentlemen, is the extraordinary marine fish. As you see, it is a fish with a very long flat head. Please observe the enormous mouth with its monstrous teeth. When it is closed, these eight long sharp fangs, which are in addition to its normal complement of teeth, remain outside. The specimen that you see here, well preserved, is the second that has ever been found."

This, more or less, was the little speech that one of the guides at the British Museum in London gave groups of visitors in 1806. In a small glass case and housed with great care, was the marine fish, known today by its scientific name of *Chauliodus sloani*.

It is a monstrous-looking animal, like other inhabitants of the depths, but disappointingly small—only eight inches long—a tiny monster, all mouth and teeth. About a hundred have been caught with special nets, at great depths, in the Mediterranean and the Atlantic Ocean.

THE TREE FROGS

THE common tree frog of Europe, North Africa, and Asia, *Hyla arborea*, is a graceful little amphibian with a remarkable ability to keep its balance on all kinds of surfaces—trees, trunks, leaves, even the smallest of twigs. Because of its musical call and its appetite for insects, it is welcome in gardens.

Day and night the tree frog follows the comings and goings of insects, small mollusks, and other tiny animals that it eats. The tree frog can stay on smooth slippery surfaces, thanks to certain expanded portions of its toes, like adhesive disks, as powerful as if they were suction cups. In the summertime it will rest on a leaf during the hottest hours of the day, hardly bending it. Green against the green leaf, it stays absolutely motionless. As soon as it gets cooler, the agile and vigilant male tree frogs inflate the huge sacs they have in their throats and begin the concerts familiar to everyone who lives in the country. It is astonishing that so much noise can come from such tiny animals, rarely as big as two inches long. Only the males are noise-makers; the females are silent.

When in the course of the year, the season for reproduction arrives, the tree frogs temporarily leave the branches and leaves of the trees. The females need water in which to lay their eggs; a pond, a brook, or a pool in a garden is sufficient. There the thousand eggs that each female can lay develop. After three months of life in the water the tadpoles have reached the last stage of their metamorphosis and become adults. They then leave their birthplace for life in the air. At the first signs of cold weather the tree frogs come down to earth and find a hole in the ground to bury themselves in. There they hibernate.

If a tree frog is well fed and kept in a moist, comfortable environment, it gets along well in captivity. They have even been known to reach the advanced age of more than twenty years. Some people believe that they can predict changes in the weather from the movements of a captive tree frog, but this is a superstition.

A tree frog in captivity needs branches, or a little ladder, or anything else on which it can climb. Otherwise, it languishes, gets thin and dies.

There are several kinds of tree frogs found in the United States. One of the most familiar is the little spring peeper whose mating calls are among the first sounds of spring in the East.

THE ALPINE NEWT

IN ancient Greek mythology, Triton was a sea deity, the son of Poseidon. Sculptors and painters have depicted him in human form down to his waist. The rest of his body is shown as a fish's tail. When his father issued the command, he blew into a conch shell trumpet. At this bellowing sound the tempests calmed down as if by a miracle, and the grateful sailors gave thanks to all the gods of Olympus, to Poseidon in particular, and, of course, did not overlook Triton.

There are a whole group of salamanders called *Triturus* or, commonly, newts. It seems hard to find any points of resemblance between the Greek deity and the newt, except that the newt leads a double life, spending most of it on land, and the other part living in the water.

One day in 1760, Lazaro Spallanzani, one of the great Italian biologists of that age, made a curious experiment. The subject was on the operating table: a magnificent newt, who seemed uncomfortable and unhappy so far from its native lake. Perhaps it was suspicious of the intentions of the illustrious operator, but the operation, although it was to cause a stir in the scientific world, promised the newt only pain.

What happened was that Spallanzani, armed with lancet and forceps, amputated the newt's limbs and then removed a large portion of its eyeballs—a veritable massacre! But miraculously, at the end of the two months, to the enormous satisfaction of the scientist (and of the animal too, no doubt) the newt was completely recovered. Not

*The newt, like the frog, is born in water and lives for
a time on land. But it returns to water to lay its eggs;
then spends part of its time in water, part on land.*

only had its amputated limbs grown back, but its eyeballs had formed anew.

Some time later another scientist froze a newt, producing apparent death, and later brought it back to life. So it is not surprising then to find the alpine newt in little lakes in the Alps, at altitudes of seven thousand feet or more.

There are other kinds of newts in Europe and in North America. One of the most common in the United States is the spotted newt. It lives in water during the early stages of its life, breathing through gills. Eventually its lungs develop and it becomes a land dweller for two or three years. During this time it is called a "red eft" because of its color. When it is ready to mate, it returns to water where it remains for the rest of its life. Its color changes to olive-green. These newts eat water insects and are especially helpful to man because they eat great numbers of mosquito larvae.

THE SILVER HATCHET

IT is thought that some fishes of the depths make frequent excursions to the surface of the water at night, going down again at daybreak to the depths, which they light up feebly with their light-producing organs, or photophores. And so fishermen will sometimes find, in a squirming mass of silvery sardines, mackerel or other edible fish, some strange creature. They will throw it back or, if they are at the dock, give it to the waiting cats, so it is never identified.

Sometimes, however, fishermen get the idea of bringing the odd fish they have chanced upon to marine biological institutes. This was what happened with a little abyssal fish found—and identified for the first time—some thirty years ago off the coast of Sicily. This tiny animal, hardly two inches long, is very broad in front and very narrow in back. On the whole it looks like a hatchet, with a sort of small handle. Because of its brilliant silvery color, it was given the Latin name of *Argyropelecus*, or silver hatchet.

As in the case with most abyssal fishes, its mouth is enormous compared with its teeth. Its huge telescopic eyes look upwards.

Its anatomical features meet the requirements of the very special conditions of the fishes' environment: the tremendous pressure of the water, the darkness, the problems of its search for food, the cold temperature of the water.

The silver hatchet has been caught in the Atlantic Ocean and in the Mediterranean Sea. It swims at various depths, from about ten thousand feet to about three hundred feet, probably in pursuit of its prey. It would not come to the surface unless caught in ascending currents that it could not resist. There near the surface await the fishermen's nets, from which museums of natural history sometimes can enrich their collections with a silver hatchet.

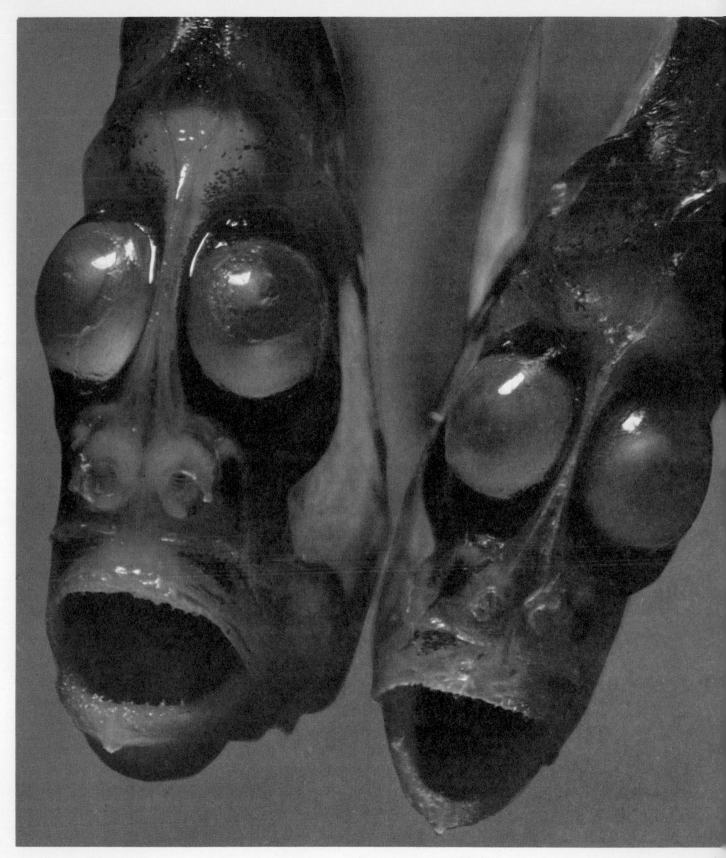

Here much magnified, but actually only two inches long, the silver hatchet inhabits the abyssal deeps of the Atlantic Ocean and the Mediterranean Sea.

PREDATORY ONES

Some animals eat only plants and fruits, some eat insects, some eat the flesh of dead animals, and some eat the flesh of animals they themselves catch and kill. Carnivores we call the flesh eaters, and predators those who prey on other living animals.

In talking about the natural world, some people are inclined to separate, say, the leaf-eating giraffe and the flesh-eating lion into opposite camps, calling one gentle, the other cruel.

In fact, however, each animal has no choice but to live as it is so adapted to or to die for not doing so. And all talk of disposition, of kindness or cruelty, is inappropriate.

THE JAGUAR

EACH tribe of South American Indians has given the jaguar a different name. Also this jungle cat is commonly called the *onça* in Brazil and *el tigre* in Spanish.

The Brazilians describe a dangerous acquaintance as "a friend of the onça (*amigo da onça*)." The cat's most common name, though, is the jaguar. This name seems to come from the Guarani dialect and to mean "body of a dog." Indeed it is a "dog" of most unusual dimensions, measuring five to seven feet from the muzzle to the root of the tail! Even if it is conceded that the jaguar's body is like a dog's, that is its only resemblance to man's favorite animal companion.

The jaguar is one of the most powerful felines in the world, and the largest one in the New World. It resembles the leopard very much in appearance, character, and habits. In the Amazon jungle, the jaguar is feared by other animals and man. The jaguar is well equipped to get itself food in abundance; with its powerful and accurate attack and with the strength of its claws, it seldom misses its prey. Almost before the victim is aware of the shock, the jaguar's claws have penetrated to a vital part of its body and it is dead.

At night, the jaguar is often on the watch near a stream where other animals might

The jaguar, shown here crouched and ready to spring, is the largest and most powerful member of the cat family found in the Americas.

come to drink. Like all cats, large and small, it moves gracefully and silently, even in the dense vegetation of the tropical forest.

As to its relations with man, opinions differ and even contradict each other. To some observers, the jaguar is only a big cat, who is afraid of man—both those who hunt with only primitive lances and arrows and those who are equipped with the most modern rifles. According to others, this cat will attack a man as fiercely as if he were a tapir or a capybara.

Among the animals of the Amazon jungle, the jaguar, a solitary predator, is the undisputed master. Even the fish, it seems, are not safe from the cat's unfailing claws. That sets the jaguar off from the other big cats, except for the true tiger of India. Only these two big cats have no aversion to water.

That is one of the few similarities between the American *el tigre* and the true tiger.

South American Indians tell stories about the way the jaguar fishes—probably not true, but certainly picturesque. They maintain that the jaguar has a technique all its own; it lures the fish by spitting. The saliva floats to the surface and attracts the unwary fish; a quick stroke of the paw and they are on

The young of a cat are its kittens, as even the junior jaguar shown here, and woe betide the man or animal who threatens to come between them.

the bank. According to another version, the jaguar uses its tail as bait, letting it hang down into the water. Actually, the fishing procedure of the jaguar is probably a good deal like that of cats trying to catch goldfish in aquariums.

All the fables told about it show the passionate interest and extreme caution that the jaguar inspires in the Indians of the South American jungles. In their legends, the jaguar is often represented as a captive —which is a way of trying to believe that this animal can be overcome.

The Tupi Indians believe that the jaguar is afraid of thunder and lightning, and interpret the animal's unrest as a sign indicating the coming of a storm. Most likely this is just the usual excitement shown by all animals, including domestic animals, when sudden atmospheric changes occur.

Here is one of the most popular Indian tales told about the jaguar:

"One day the Jaguar came upon the Lightning, who was making a club. The

Jaguar came up from behind and the Lightning did not see him. He leaped at the Lightning but could not get to him. He thought the Lightning was an animal and wanted to eat him. The Jaguar asked the Lightning if he had any strength, and the Lightning answered that he had none. Then the Jaguar said, 'I am not like you. I have great strength and I can break all the branches. Just see!' And he climbed a caimbé tree and broke all its branches. Then he climbed a parica tree and broke all its branches, too. Then he came down to the ground and tore up all the grass, ripping up the earth with his claws. Finally he got tired and rested. Panting, he said, 'See how strong I am! I am not like you!' Secretly, he intended to devour the Lightning, and he invited him to show his strength, but the Lightning refused, saying, 'I am not like you; I have no strength!' Then the Jaguar

Neither water nor the top of a tree is a safe refuge from the prowling and predacious jaguar. But it was probably the quest not of prey but of comfort that brought the oddly matched pair at left (a black jaguar is rare) to dunk themselves.

35

said again, 'Look at me; see how strong I am!' And he did the same things he had done before. He tore off the branches, tore up the grass, and ripped up the earth. Then he got tired and sat alongside the Lightning, turning his back on him.

"The Lightning took his little club, waved it, and everything happened at once: thunder, flashes of lightning, wind and rain. The Jaguar climbed a tree, but the Lightning knocked down all the trees and the Jaguar fell to the ground. The Lightning took him by the paw and swung him around. The Jaguar escaped and hid under a rock, but the Lightning caught up with him, struck the rock and forced him to come out. Then he climbed another tree, but the Lightning knocked down that tree. The Jaguar fled to a cave, but the Lightning caught up with him there too, and made the earth cave in. And the Jaguar had no more peace; the Lightning was always pursuing him. Then it became very cold, with wind and rain, so that the Jaguar was chilled and could not run any longer, and finally curled up on the ground. When the Lightning saw him in such a sad state, he said, 'You see, my friend, what I am like! I am strong, too! You are not the only one that is strong; I think I am stronger than you are!' And he went off. The Jaguar went back to his den. But ever since then, all Jaguars are afraid of thunderstorms."

This legend confirms the popular reputation that the jaguar has for courage and aggressiveness. Some Indian tribes will not even use the skin of a jaguar that they have killed, as if the death of this predator was enough of a blessing and it would be dangerous to try to make further profit from it. Certain tribes, however, make use of jaguar teeth; they burn them and grind them into powder, using the powder as a remedy for toothache and other dental problems.

Sometimes a jaguar is unwary and is caught in a trap, generally a big and deep pit, covered with branches. The cat is then brought to a zoo in a strong cage. It may resign itself to imprisonment if it is well fed, but it retains its proud, untamable spirit.

THE HARPY EAGLE

THE harpy eagle may be named for the Harpies of ancient Greek mythology. The Harpies were creatures with the heads of women and the bodies of birds of prey. These legendary Harpies were sent to punish people by carrying off their food. However, this superb bird of Central and South America does not really resemble the Harpies of mythology.

Their strange name may come from the Greek "harpazein" which means "to seize." The Greeks called falcons and kites "harpe." The Roman naturalist Pliny calls the vulture "harpe" as well.

The harpy eagle, like these other birds, is a bird of prey. It is about three feet long, and its body is covered with magnificent plumage. The head and neck are soft gray;

The harpy eagle, found from southern Mexico to northern Argentina, is a menace both to the animals that run on the ground and to the monkeys that inhabit the forest tops.

the crest, wings, tail and upper part of the body are a handsome slate-gray; the underparts are white, as are the feathers on the legs. The beak and claws are dark and the skin of the legs is yellowish. The birds' bright eyes are constantly alert. The harpy eagle's head has a double crest of feathers which the bird can raise or lower at will.

Small creatures of the jungle are defenseless against the lightning speed of the harpy eagle, and few animals are able to enter into competition with it. It flies tirelessly above the tall trees or perches on a high branch, almost hidden in the dense foliage. When it has sighted its prey, whether this be a macaw, a monkey, or a sloth, the eagle drops down on it with incredible speed through intertwined branches, lianas and bushes, and seizes it in its strong claws. The eagle's feet and talons are so big that they almost seem out of proportion with the rest of the bird's body.

Thus armed for the struggle, this constant struggle, that puts natural selection into operation at every moment within the teeming life of tropical forests, the harpy eagle probably dies a natural death, unless some disease or injury weakens it so that it becomes the victim of another predator.

Most of the Indian tribes in the basin of the Amazon regard the harpy eagle as an honorable enemy. The blood, fat and droppings of the bird are used as bases for native medicines, supposedly good for a number of diseases. The Indian who is skillful or lucky enough to bring down a harpy eagle does not let anyone forget the fact. He adorns his head with the big strong feathers from the wings and tail of his trophy.

Finding a nest of this bird is a very difficult enterprise, although the nest is large and sturdy. The harpy eagle nests in as high a tree as possible, in well-hidden, almost inaccessible spots. The female lays two eggs. As with most eagles, the young stay in the nest for a long period before they are able to fly. Both parents help feed the young. The harpy eagles do well in captivity and are found in many zoos.

THE CAIMAN

SOME animals seem impossible to classify at a glance. One of these is the caiman. A traveler, finding one near a stream in a Brazilian forest, might scream, "A crocodile!" and flee. The caiman is not a crocodile, although it belongs to the order Crocodilia. It also belongs to the sub-family Alligatorinae. Crocodiles are found in Asia, Africa, Australia, and tropical America; one species of alligators lives in the United States and one in China; caimans live in Central and South America.

There are more than one species of caiman. A distinction must be made among the spectacled caiman, the jacaré caiman and several others.

The spectacled caiman has a kind of armor on its back that seems to be made of heavy coins, thick enough to resist bullets. If one has to be killed, it must be shot in the side, where its armor is weakest. The adjective "spectacled" was given to it because the transverse ridge above its eyes gives the illusion, when seen directly from the front, that the caiman is wearing a pair of spectacles with frames on them. Its eyes can be seen at once, whereas its teeth can not. It has them though, eighty of them—and very strong ones.

The caiman stays on land during the day for hours on end, without going very far from the water—the river, lake or pond that is its hunting ground. Half-buried in the tall grass, it sleeps for hours, only getting up when it is hungry again. It gets into the

Neither crocodile nor alligator is the scaly caiman which, full grown as above, or newly hatched and hatching as below, looks quite a bit like both.

water with the slow clumsy gait that is characteristic also of crocodiles and alligators. At first the caiman does not seem to be a good swimmer, but appears to be content with staying on the surface, letting the upper part of its head, the eyes and nostrils, emerge. These slow and quiet movements are only a feint. If the caiman went through the water at full speed, as it does sometimes when it has to, there would be a good chance it would not catch anything it cared to sink its teeth into; while, if it is motionless, it arouses no suspicion. Those eight feet of floating scales, with no sign of life, look remarkably like a log. Many a fish, mollusk

and small amphibian continue their quiet life in the pool with no fear whatever, until they are within reach of the huge mouth that swallows them immediately.

Then the caiman will turn again and go slowly up the bank. It has sighted a marsh bird preening its feathers, feet out of the water. There is hardly a flutter of the bird's wings, as the enormous animal makes its killing with incredible speed. However, things are not so easy on land for the spectacled caiman. It is up against faster animals that are very dangerous to it. There is the jaguar, for instance, who treats the reptile as it would any big lizard, and sometimes

kills it. And then there are men, with their dangerous firearms or even simple nooses.

Capturing a caiman is not a simple task. A stout rope has to be placed around the animal's neck and then pulled tight. Thereafter, the caiman may be taken to a zoo.

If the noose has been held by some of the Indians of the Amazonian jungle, the caiman may finish up as a roast. Its skin has long been valued for making fine leather goods, and there is an extensive market for it in many parts of the world.

The caiman is born from an egg the size of a duck's egg, which its mother had buried in the sand. As soon as the young animal is in the open air, it turns instinctively toward the water. Not very stable on its weak legs, it often becomes entangled in the dense tropical vegetation and has great difficulty in covering the short distance to safety. This is the baby caiman's most dangerous time. Sometimes it will be seized in the sharp beak of a bird, sometimes by the sharp teeth of a carnivore, and sometimes it will be eaten by an adult caiman. Finally, four or five little caimans to a particular brood arrive at their watery goal, safe and sound. Most of them will end up as food for a predator within the first few years of their lives, but a few will grow up to be eight-foot-long adult caimans.

Like many animals, the caiman is benefited in its struggle for survival by a natural camouflage, which allows it to blend in with the colors of its surroundings, such as the murky shadowed waters pictured at the far left. Pity, though, the unwary fish or amphibian which strays near the caiman's still, dark shape, taking it for merely another log. Its gums bristle with teeth, eighty pointed pieces of ivory, and it waits there only for the chance to put them to good use.

41

*When it is full grown, the snowy owl has few nat-
ural enemies. And it is just as well it doesn't,
for, in the Arctic, finding food is trouble enough.*

THE SNOWY OWL

THE birds of the order Strigiformes are owls of all kinds: barn owls, screech owls, horned owls. Owls have been used as symbols of wisdom; they have been considered also as birds of ill omen. This superstitious fear is probably due to their silent flight, to the disconcerting stare of their big round eyes, to their nocturnal habits, to their mournful cry, to their hooked beak, and to the almost human expressions which they sometimes have. In the literature of fantasy, every witch's den must have an owl as part of its equipment, and the same is true for haunted castles, where owls always watch from the battlements.

More realistic and better-informed lovers of animals and nature have done much to protect these innocent and useful creatures. On the basis of overwhelming factual data, they have had laws passed to protect the owls. Regardless of the aspect of these birds, be it beautiful or ugly, there is no doubt about the services owls render to agricul-

ture, because they destroy an enormous quantity of small rodents such as field mice, and voles, and rabbits. For this reason the hunting of owls by men, either by trapping or shooting, is now prohibited by law in many states.

The night-flying and night-calling owls, about which man has invented so many mysterious and even sinister tales, live in the temperate regions. But in the arctic regions of the world, the snowy owl flies by day, merging with the dazzling whiteness of the snow-covered tundra. This magnificent owl passes its life in the arctic tundra, with the exception of a short period in the middle of each winter, when it makes a seasonal migratory trip to the forests at the tundra's edge.

Magnificent is an apt word for the snowy owl. It stands about twenty-five inches tall and its soft, thick plumage covers its entire body, except for the talons. Some birds are nearly all white; others are flecked with

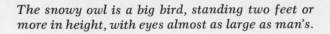

the sea—the ones that are left are said to rush into the waters and swim to their death. The lemmings do not reproduce regularly in the same numbers, so the snowy owl is not always sure of finding enough of them to provide it with nourishment. Therefore, the owl has to look for other animals, such as arctic hare, ducks, and, less often, the ptarmigan, for food. When the food supplies are low in the Far North, the snowy owls may migrate southward during the winter months. They then appear in northern United States, in Great Britain and in northern Europe.

The adult snowy owl has practically no enemies in its arctic home, except for man. The baby owls, on the other hand, are endangered by the arctic fox, and especially so because the nest they live in is very rudimentary. It is usually on top of a small rise in the tundra. In the hollow of the nest are the white eggs, about seven in good years when the food is plentiful, about two or three in years when food is scarce. Only the female sits on the nest, but her mate stays nearby. The female watches over the newly hatched young with great care; she and the male supply food to the brood. The mother bird protects her young from the arctic cold by covering them with her ventral feathers and with her outspread wings.

The snowy owl is wary of man, who brings it only death or captivity. It usually does not do well in captivity.

On rare occasions, the Eskimos eat the meat of this beautiful bird. It is very hard to trap, and shooting it in flight calls for great skill on the part of the hunter.

brownish-black feathers. Its eyes are an unusually bright yellow, with a black ring surrounding the iris.

These birds hunt mainly by day. The tundra does not provide the same abundance of game that the forest does, and hunger is a constant menace. Fortunately for this handsome, strong-flying bird of prey, there are the lemmings, very lively little rodents whose flesh is one of the birds' main foods. But the lemmings have a periodic increase of population which causes their mass migrations to the south. During such migrations, a large number of lemmings disappear, either as prey for other animals, or because of starvation or illness. Finally the lemmings' migrations may come to an end when these little creatures meet

44

THE PUMA

THE puma is a carnivorous mammal, a member of the cat family which includes such magnificent animals as the jaguar, the lion, the tiger, and the leopard.

Other names for the puma are cougar, mountain lion, and catamount. It is only found in North, Central and South America.

This large handsome cat has a solid-colored tawny coat, without spots, and is almost as big as a lioness, being thirty inches high at the shoulder and almost seven feet long, including twenty-five to thirty inches of tail. It weighs up to two hundred pounds. Its head is small and graceful, and its golden eyes are very expressive. The solid muscles of the puma's body give it a rapid, powerful spring.

In western United States it usually lives in rocky terrains. It climbs trees well. Pumas live a roving solitary life, walking abroad at dusk under the cover of the brush or trees. It attacks small mammals, elk, deer, and sometimes even domestic farm animals. At one time pumas were found in most parts of the United States. Now, however, they have been hunted to extinction in most parts of the country. As a result, their normal prey, such as deer, have multiplied to the point where they cannot always find enough to eat. Many deer die of famine in the winter.

The puma or cougar of South America lives in jungles as well as in mountainous areas. It hunts monkeys in the forest, chasing them through the trees.

In the early spring litters of from two to five young are born. They have yellow fur with dark spots during the first six months of their life. They stay with their mother for about two years.

The puma is curious about man, but seldom if ever attacks him.

At one time found in most parts of the United States, the puma has been hunted to the edge of extinction.

THE KING VULTURE

THE king vulture is distinguished from the large number of other vultures by its brilliant plumage and its unusual appearance. Most American vultures are brown or black; the king vulture is a striking cream and black. It lives in Central and South America, usually in rather forested regions.

The Andean condor, which is much larger than the king vulture, is also found in South America but mainly in the Andes. This condor has a wingspread of about ten feet. The wingspread of the king vulture is about seven feet. Both birds, needless to say, are impressive in flight. The contrasting colors of the king vulture's naked head are amazingly beautiful. The black of the beak becomes a clear reddish at the end. The rest of the skin on the head is a mixture of reds, purples, and yellows. Only adult birds have this vivid head coloring. The feathers on the back, the abdomen and the thighs are a soft cream. The lower part of the wings and the big tail feathers are a dark, iridescent greenish-blue.

King vultures, like other vultures, wait for the sun to warm the air before they begin their circling flight. Soaring on thermal updrafts, they are constantly on the lookout for dead animals. Because of their relatively weak feet, they cannot catch their own prey. When they spy carrion on the ground, they come down to feed. Many vultures will often feed at the same time and roost together at night in the same trees. Like all the members of their family, they perform a very useful job of sanitation.

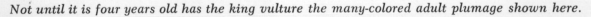

Not until it is four years old has the king vulture the many-colored adult plumage shown here.

With a prehensile tail and tough claws, the two-toed anteater is well suited to an arboreal life.

THE TWO-TOED ANTEATER

THE two-toed anteater is not as clumsy as its relative, the giant anteater. In view of its small size, about twelve inches in length, and its numerous enemies, which include poisonous snakes and man, the two-toed anteater has long since taken security precautions. It lives in the trees and comes down as little as possible, especially in the daytime. It feeds at night.

Even at that, its life is often endangered; but still it is safer most of the time than the animals that live on the ground. The dense foliage of the Amazon jungle affords a certain amount of protection for an animal that has neither skill nor agility.

The two-toed anteater finds the ants and termites that it lives on among the branches of the trees. It opens the termites' nests with

Ants and termites, whose nests it opens with its claws, are the main fare of the two-toed anteater.

the two-clawed toes of its front paws, and eats the fleeing insects, scooping them up with its long sticky tongue.

Any animal who lives in the treetops is in danger of falling. The two-toed anteater hooks its long prehensile tail around a branch; thus anchored, it can dine at ease.

When the sun rises, the two-toed anteater faces the problem of finding a shelter where it will be well concealed during the day. Sometimes it hides in a hole in a tree. If no hole is available it will look for a branch protected by foliage. It sleeps hanging down from the branch, holding on by its feet and tail, merging with its surroundings. It then looks like a tawny-colored fruit. Its appearance and immobility while asleep help protect it from predators.

THE GREAT ANTEATER

THE great anteater is a very strange-looking animal. It almost looks like a mistake of nature, as do most anteaters. None of the parts of its body seem to go with the others.

Its very long head ends in a long nozzle-shaped snout. At the end of its snout is an inconspicuous slit, less than half an inch wide, which is its mouth. Another remarkable feature of the giant anteater is its tongue. It is round like a tube, twelve inches long and half an inch wide. This tongue is covered with a sticky substance.

48

The giant anteater's four-foot-long body is borne on four legs that do not match: the front ones are strong and short, the hind ones longer and larger. The front legs have strong, sharp, curved claws—the middle

However strange an animal may seem to us, there is always a reason for it. The long narrow head and sticky eel-like tongue of the great anteater equip it to do best the thing for which it has been named: eat ants, and similar insects.

claw may measure up to three inches in length. These claws make an effective weapon for defense.

When it walks, the giant anteater bends the claws of its front legs and walks on their outer surface. At night it waddles clumsily through the forest, pretty much at random, snout to the ground, searching for ants and termites. It has weak eyes and depends on its sense of smell to lead it to anthills and to termite nests, which it demolishes with powerful blows of its claws. Then it gathers up hundreds of these insects with its sticky tongue. After its meal, the anteater retires to a shelter under dense foliage, rolls itself up into a ball and covers its body with its bushy tail. It sleeps peaceably most of the day.

Adult females have a single offspring each year. The baby anteaters are carried about on their mother's back at first, and stay with her for about one year.

THE OCELOT

MEN have called certain cats "mysterious" because of cats' impenetrable gaze. The domestic cat used to be considered an ally of sorcerers, and even as a bit of a sorcerer itself. The adjective "lazy" might be applied to its blissful way of stretching and yawning when it is sleepy. If the perfect proportions of its body are considered, as well as its admirable adaptation to nearly all circumstances, the adjective "elegant" could certainly be used. Mysterious, lazy, elegant—a cat is all of these and many other things besides. But above all the cat is a predator, an efficient and well-armed hunter, a professional in the art of ambush. The only cat that hunts on the run is the cheetah.

All cats have the same highly specialized teeth. They lack the crushing molars, but the incisors, canines and premolars are perfectly adapted tools for cutting the flesh of their prey. Cats' curved, pointed claws are fearful weapons. And, since these claws are retractable, except in the cheetah, they do not wear down because of constant contact with the ground. In addition to these weapons, cats have remarkable senses of smell and hearing. They also have a keen sense of sight and can, of course, see in the dark. But not all cats have the same degree of perfection of these natural aptitudes.

The cat is an individualistic, reserved animal, which always guards its independence. These feline characteristics are all found in the ocelot, in the wild state. Naturalists do not know too much about the behavior of the ocelot in its natural habitat because it is a very difficult animal to observe. First of all it is exclusively nocturnal in habit. During the day it sleeps in its den. Then it chooses the most remote sections of the forest for its refuge. There it has practically no rivals.

The area over which the ocelot occurs is from southern Texas, where it is now rare,

Elegant in motion, fierce in battle, and always wary, the ocelot is a skilled and cunning hunter which often sets upon its quarry from an ambush.

through Mexico to Central and South America. There are several different races of ocelots which vary in size and color.

The ocelot is a patient, wily and able hunter. It finds its prey among small mammals. It will also eat snakes, birds and even monkeys when it can catch them. The mating period is not definitely known, but it is probably in early summer. The litter is usually limited to two cubs. Ocelots are sometimes killed for their magnificent fur, which is highly valued. Capturing adults for zoos is difficult; the ocelot scents the traps and passes warily by. However, young ocelots are supposed to be easy to tame.

The ocelot is usually about three feet long including its tail. It has a bright pink nose.

Native to North and South America, the ocelot does its sleeping by day and its hunting by night.

USEFUL SNAKES

TRADITIONALLY, snakes are animals towards which man has shown a profound aversion. This crawling animal arouses man's fear and repugnance, and seems to represent to him a menace against which he would find it difficult to protect himself. The cold, unwavering glance of the snake's immobile eyes does not inspire affection. And yet one cannot say that snakes are ugly. If man did not have such a deep-seated prejudice against snakes, he would admire their elegance, their splendid and varied colors, and their marvelous motion. Another thing which should be kept in mind is that many snakes are not poisonous or dangerous but

that, on the contrary, they are very useful to farmers and are even protected in some countries.

Members of the Colubrine family, the largest family of snakes, are found nearly everywhere in the world. Most of them are not poisonous. They eat rodents, especially rats and mice. Some members of this family are even called rat snakes. There are five kinds of rat snakes found in the United States.

The bull snake, or gopher snake as it is called on the Pacific Coast, is about six feet long and is yellowish-brown in color with symmetrical brown spots. When surprised, this snake coils, hisses and even rattles its tail. If a farmer in mid-western United States is having his crops eaten by rodents, he tries to catch bull snakes and put them in his fields. After the bull snake is let loose, it is not long before the farmer's crops no longer suffer from the rodents. The bull snake follows its prey down into the depths of their burrows, crushes them in its powerful coils and eats them. Above ground it also kills its prey by constriction.

Other snakes which aid in the control of rodents are the corn snakes, yellowish-brown with red spots, the pilot black snakes and the coachwhip snakes. The coachwhip snakes were given that name because they look like whips used by coachmen.

Whatever the reason for man's aversion to snakes, it is often inappropriate, for many snakes are helpful to man, preying on things that are not.

In India, many folk tales are told about the Indian rat snake. It sometimes grows to eight feet in length and is supposed to be a welcome visitor in houses infested with rats and mice.

The rat snakes of Madagascar are of great help to the sugar plantation owners because the snakes keep the rodent population under control. Otherwise the rodents would do great damage to the sugar cane crops on that island.

The indigo snake, handsomer and more amiable in character than the bull snake, is also entitled to the farmer's gratitude. If man could get used to these inoffensive creatures and overcome his repulsion, he would do justice to allies that make few demands on him.

The king snakes will attack and eat other snakes, including the poisonous rattlesnakes. The king snake almost always comes out the victor in these combats, especially if the rattlesnake is smaller. The king snake seems immune to the rattlesnake's venom. The king snake kills its adversary by strangling it in its coils, and then eats it, starting with the victim's head. In addition to snakes, the king snake will eat rats, small animals and birds. There are about fifteen species of king snakes found in North America.

THE SHARKS

Sharks are classified as fishes although their skeletons are cartilaginous; that is, made of gristle, rather than bone, as are the skeletons of most other fishes. They also differ from bony fishes in many other ways. Most sharks give birth to live young, although a few lay eggs. There are more than two hundred species of sharks.

The great white shark is one of the largest sharks. It can be up to thirty feet in length and weigh about two tons, although the usual length is about ten feet. Its head has the typical shape of the species, terminating, well below the snout, in an enormous transverse mouth. Within its very powerful jaws are triangular teeth like those of a saw. With this equipment and an insatiable appetite, it is not content with mollusks and plankton, but is armed to attack all kinds of animals from man to seals, and spreads terror in the world of fishes.

The white shark, and all sharks in general, are elongated and spindle-shaped. They have great muscular power. This power and the large fins give them tremendous speed, matched by few other aquatic animals.

Sharks live chiefly in warm ocean waters, but there are some in colder regions. Some even go up rivers and a few are found in fresh-water lakes. Some seize anything they come across; others eat small sea animals, plankton, and plants.

The stories told by seamen and explorers have given rise to many legends about these animals, such as the myth of small ships being crushed and their crews gulped down

The bad reputation that all sharks have was actually earned by just a few kinds. For all there are in the ocean, only relatively few sharks do approach the shore, and they are not apt to attack a swimmer unless there is provocation.

by sharks. It is a fact, however, that some kinds of hungry sharks will unhesitatingly swallow virtually anything, and that they attack indiscriminately, even coming close inshore at beaches, terrifying swimmers. According to recent statistics, sharks have caused the death of some forty victims in the last ten years. The number of deaths seem to be increasing, possibly because of the popularity of skin diving. All sorts of alien inedible objects—wooden beams, empty

The thresher shark has a very long tail fin. It waves this fin back and forth in the water and thus stuns small fish which the shark then eats. Sometimes a team of threshers will work together to keep a school of fish in an inlet while the sharks feed on them. Thresher sharks are found in temperate as well as in warm waters.

The most unusual looking shark is the hammerhead. Its flat, hammer-shaped head extends out beyond each side of its body.

The normal feeding hours of a shark, when they are most dangerous, are around sunrise and sunset. Other times they keep to the bottom or, not infrequently, cruise near the top, with perhaps just their dorsal and tail fins cutting the surface.

kegs, and even rubber tires—have been found in the stomachs of captured sharks. The shark is guided to its prey by its sense of smell. The slightest trace of blood attracts it at once.

The tiger shark is smaller than the white shark, but just as dangerous, fierce and aggressive. It is hunted as are many sharks, for its liver. An oil is obtained from shark liver that has great therapeutic value because of its high vitamin content. The tiger shark is usually found swimming near the surface of warm ocean waters.

In general, most sharks are animals that it is well for man to avoid. The basking shark is an exception. The first one to be captured, in 1828, caused a sensation because of its tremendous size; but despite its dimensions, it does not have the predatory nature of other sharks. The average basking shark is about thirty feet long. It has many small teeth and it lives on small sea animals and plankton. It was a basking shark, a veritable sea monster, that followed the famous raft, the Kon-Tiki, for some time during its epic crossing of the Pacific Ocean. All the shark

did was to escort the raft until it lost interest in this strange floating object; it made no attempt to attack the raft, no doubt much to the relief of the raft's occupants.

The skin of sharks is hard and thick. It is used to make fine leather goods. Sharks are covered with small scales, each ending in a sharp curved "tooth." The resemblance to human teeth is astonishing. Each "tooth" on a scale has a pulp cavity with nerves and blood vessels and is covered with enamel. If a scale is lost a new one grows in to replace it. Before these scales are removed from it,

sharkskin is called shagreen. Shagreen is sometimes used for sanding wood.

There are two fish that have no fear of sharks. One, called the pilot fish, is often found in the immediate vicinity of sharks, feeding on the scraps of food left by them. The pilot fish is about sixteen inches long, and looks tiny alongside the shark. The other fish, the remora, or shark-sucker, has a suction disc on its head. It attaches itself by this disc to the body of a shark and hitches a ride. It also feeds on leavings from the shark's meals.

QUIET ONES

There is no evil in the natural world, nothing that is naturally good or naturally bad. For, where there is no choice given, there is no evil way, no good or bad, and that is the situation in the natural world. All the animals in it, except man, lack the refinement of intellect required to decide for good or evil. The actions of animals are instinctive, and have been successful thus far in perpetuating the species. Man alone seems to have the power to rise above or fall below the instinctive behavior that governs the natural world.

Yet man's power to understand behavior brings with it the hazard of misunderstanding, and much in nature has been misunderstood by him. The snake, for example, is considered evil by many people, sinister in purpose and appearance. The silence with which it moves is thought to be part of its evil design. In reality, this is a self-protective measure, built into the life-habit of the snake, enabling it to get food and to move about without endangering itself.

THE EMERALD TREE BOA

THE boas live mainly in the tropics of the New World. There are some fifty or more species, ranging in size from the giant anaconda, which may reach a length of thirty feet, to the small rubber boa which is only two feet long. The emerald tree boa, one of the most attractive members of the boa family, is about four feet long when it is full-grown.

The female emerald tree boa, like all other boas, does not lay eggs but gives birth to young. Young emerald tree boas are red, but the adults are a brilliant green, with yellow or white bands on their back. Since these snakes live mainly in trees in the forests of northern South America, their brilliant colors blend in perfectly with those of their surroundings.

One of the most beautifully colored of all snakes is the emerald tree boa, which is native to the northern part of South America.

In its mouth, it has long sharp teeth, from which it gets its scientific name of *Boa canina*. But a boa's bite is not poisonous. They use their teeth to hold the small animals they catch, while they constrict their prey within the coils of their bodies. They eat birds and lizards and small mammals

a powerful paw at the snake's most vulnerable part, the head.

Even for a snake, the equatorial forest is full of dangers and it has no assurance of leading a long and peaceful life. Perhaps that is why boas do not seem homesick in zoos. They may not have complete freedom

The jaws of the emerald tree boa, shut (left) *or wide open* (right), *are less of a menace than the long green body trailing after them which, coiled around a branch* (bottom right) *is harmless enough, but coiled around an animal can kill it.*

that wander within their reach. Their jaws can be extended so that they can swallow an animal that may be wider than the width of their own heads.

Boas spend much of their time sleeping. When a boa is disturbed, it coils itself around a branch. It does not try to escape; it neither attacks nor pursues. Its only reaction is to become immobile.

Those animals which seem to be aware of the power of the boa's crushing grip may then ignore it. But the jaguar, aggressive as always, will not accept this immobility and may let fly at the reptile with a blow of

there, but they will not encounter their enemy, the jaguar.

The Cook's tree boa resembles the emerald boa in certain ways, especially in its habits, but it is a golden-brown color. It hides so well among the leaves and branches of trees that it can hardly be seen.

The most famous boa is probably the boa constrictor, which lives in Central and northern South America. This snake is about ten feet long.

The anaconda, not only the largest boa, but thought also to be the largest snake of the New World, lives in the tropical forests

60

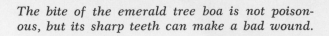

of South America. It is usually found near water, either along rivers or in marshes. It eats mammals as well as birds and reptiles.

There are even two boas found in western United States. One, the rosy boa, lives in Southern California and Mexico. It is a small striped snake about three feet long. It makes its home in dry rocky areas and eats rodents. The other boa, the rubber boa, is smaller. It also eats rodents and lizards. This brownish-gray boa lives mainly in forests of the Northwest but its range extends to California.

THE CRABS

CRABS seem to have no head because they have no neck. Their body is protected by a carapace, a shell, from which five pairs of claws emerge. The first pair of claws have pincers on them.

This very valuable carapace is also a recurrent source of danger to the crab. The crab cannot grow while it is enclosed in its shell. For this reason, periodically during its years of growth, it must molt the old shell and replace it with a new one. In the short period from the time the crab sheds its old shell until the time the new shell hardens the crab is without protection. It must also grow to a larger size in this interval—which it manages to do by taking in large quantities of water and expanding its body. Most crabs try to stay hidden until they have new

hard shells, but many are lost to predators at this crucial stage.

The crab is surrounded by enemies because its meat is sought for, not only by man, but by all sorts of animals: birds, fish and octopuses. Accordingly, it tries to escape notice as much as possible. Many crabs are camouflaged so that it is difficult to see them in their natural environment. For example the crab *Dromia vulgaris* has a large number of spines on its carapace. These become covered with little pebbles, algae, shellfish, and pieces of sponge. Thus the crab merges with its surroundings and is almost invisible.

Crabs usually move sideways, but they also walk backward or forward. When trying to escape danger, they travel quickly.

The rock crabs of the northeastern coasts of the United States remain motionless among rocks during the day or else dig a hole in the sand with their powerful pincer claws and bury themselves completely. At night they come out hunting for food. They eat a wide variety of food, both living and dead, animal and plant.

The most dangerous enemies of crabs that live in the ocean are the octopus and the dorado, or dolphin fish. The octopus paralyzes the crab with its tentacles, which cover it with a sticky liquid. The dorado uses its teeth to attack the crab's carapace; once a hole has been made, the fish eats the crab's flesh. The crab can not defend itself unless the dorado attacks one of its claws. In that case the crab sheds the limb and escapes. The claw will grow on again at the crab's next molt. The dorado only attacks smaller species of crabs.

The largest crab known is the Japanese spider crab. Its very long legs may measure ten feet from claw to claw. Smaller species of spider crabs are found along the Atlantic and Pacific coasts of North America. These crabs get their name from their small bodies and very long legs.

One of the most familiar European species is the tourteau or edible crab of the Atlantic and the North Sea; it is rare in the Mediterranean. It can be up to two feet across and weigh as much as thirteen pounds. During the Eocene epoch it was very common in all the seas of the world, and fossil specimens of it have been found almost everywhere.

Along the Atlantic coast in the western hemisphere the best crab for food is the blue crab. It lives not only in the ocean, but is also found in brackish and even freshwater rivers along the coast. "Soft-shelled crabs" are blue crabs caught and used for food at the time of their molt; their new shells have not had a chance to harden. They are eaten shell and all.

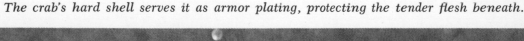

The crab's hard shell serves it as armor plating, protecting the tender flesh beneath.

Some crabs live on beaches, burrowing into the sand. One of these is the fiddler crab. The male fiddler crab has one very large claw which it uses to attract a mate and to fight other male fiddler crabs during the mating season. If this large claw should be lost to a predator, it will be replaced at the crab's next molt, but on the opposite side of the body.

Fiddler crabs usually dig their burrows in the sand between the areas of the beach covered with water at high tide and dry at low tide. When the tide goes out, the crabs come out of their holes to feed. Since they eat during the day, it is possible to observe them on isolated beaches. If they are disturbed, they run back to their burrows.

Fiddler crabs eat organic matter which they find in the sand. Females use their two small claws to roll this material into little pellets. The males use only their single small claws for eating, never their large claws. Before the tide comes in, the crabs return to their holes and close up the entrances. They rest there until the next low tide.

Young fiddlers and adult females are brownish-gray, as are adult males when they first come out of their burrows. However, during the day, in some species, the males' shells gradually change so that they are almost white with orange-yellow claws. If they are caught, their color changes back to gray-brown, as it also does at the end of the day. These color changes are caused by hormones in the crabs' bodies.

Fiddler crabs are often quite small creatures. Some measure about one inch across their shell and a little less than that from head to back.

Sand or ghost crabs are also burrowing crabs. It is almost impossible to see them on sand because of their protective coloring. However, they usually come out to feed only at night when they are relatively safe from shore birds.

There are also many species of land crabs, especially in the tropics. Although they must live their early life in the sea, breathing through gills, as adults they live on land. During the day they hide under rocks and logs, coming out at night to look for food.

The hermit crabs are not true crabs because they lack shells. In order to protect themselves they use discarded sea shells such as those of periwinkles and whelks. As the hermit crabs grow, they have to find new and bigger shell "houses." When these crabs walk around, they carry their shells with them. The largest hermit crab is the coconut or robber crab. It is able to open a coconut with its claws and may even climb up coconut trees to cut down the nuts. It lives on South Pacific islands.

THE IGUANAS

IGUANAS are those lizards that belong to the Iguanidae family. There are about seven hundred species of them. They are found only in the New World, in certain islands in the South Pacific, and in Madagascar.

In eastern United States the most common iguana is the fence lizard. It is grayish-brown but has blue scales underneath its body. It was given its name because it is often seen running along fences or resting in the sun on them.

Western iguanas include the horned lizards, the sand lizards, and the utas. The horned lizards, or horned toads as they are sometimes called, may, if frightened, squirt a small amount of blood from their eyes. The utas are among the smallest iguanas, the adults measuring only about five inches in total length.

Another interesting iguana of the Southwest is the chuckwalla. If an enemy threatens it, it hides in between rocks and inflates its body. The enemy finds that it is almost impossible to pull the inflated chuckwalla out of its hiding place.

The anoles are a fascinating group of iguanas. They are found in tropical or subtropical regions. Depending on the temperature and light, they can change their color from brown to green. The males have a red skin flap on their throats which they inflate during courtship or as a warning to other males to keep out of their territory.

The largest iguanas are the common iguanas which live in tropical Central and South America. They may be as long as six feet including their tails, but the tails account for about two-thirds of the total length. They look like animals which have survived from the earliest days of the earth.

Common iguanas are vegetarians; they eat leaves and fruit. With their strong claws they can easily climb to the highest limbs of the tropical forest trees. The females lay their eggs in the ground; the young iguanas hatch in about two months.

People who live in the regions where the common iguanas are found consider them to be a great food delicacy. The iguanas, however, are not easy to capture since they

can escape by climbing, by running, or even by swimming.

Two of the rarest iguanas live in the Galapagos Islands off the coast of South America. The first of these is the marine iguana, the only iguana which feeds on seaweed. One of their favorite foods is sea lettuce. They are excellent swimmers, but usually feed close to shore at low tide. After they eat, they spend the rest of the day basking in the sun along the rocky coast.

Most of the marine iguanas are blackish like the volcanic rock on which they live. However, on some of the islands the iguanas have patches of red or green during the mating season. At this time too, there are apt to be head-butting battles between males and even between females looking for places in the sand where they could lay their eggs. Each female lays only two eggs —some other species of iguanas may lay as many as eighty eggs—which hatch in about two and a half months. Newly hatched marine iguanas are about ten or eleven inches long; adults may be from three to four feet in length.

The other Galapagos iguanas are the land iguanas which are from two to four feet long. They live on cacti and other plants. Their numbers have been greatly reduced by dogs, by pigs which eat iguana eggs, and by humans who use them for food.

From these two photographs, *the difference between the land* (above) *and marine* (below) *iguanas of the Galapagos Islands may be easily observed.*

Scattered upon the surface of a seaside ledge, motionless in the heat of a brilliant noonday sun, are (left) hundreds of the darkly colored marine iguanas, native to the Galapagos Islands.

There are two species of land iguanas found on different islands of the Galapagos. In one species the males become red and yellow during certain seasons; in the other species there is no color change from the usual yellowish-brown.

In 1964, leading scientists of many countries established the Darwin Research Station in the Galapagos. One of the purposes of this biological station is to find out, by studying various plant and animal interrelations, what conservation measures are necessary to save the rare and unique animals of these islands, including the land iguanas.

There are now thriving colonies of these only on two of the eight islands.

Both the marine and the land iguanas of the Galapagos were first described by Charles Darwin in his *Journal*. He visited the Galapagos early in the nineteenth century, on a trip around the world.

NEW WORLD MONKEYS

Charles Darwin, with whose words this section opens and closes, is held in disrepute by some for having made the suggestion that man was related to some far-distant monkey-like ancestor. Darwin himself did not find it objectionable for, as he wrote: "I would as soon be descended from that heroic little monkey, who braved his dreaded enemy in order to save the life of his keeper, . . . as from a savage who delights to torture his enemies, offers up bloody sacrifices, practices infanticide without remorse, treats his wives like slaves, knows no decency, and is haunted by the grossest superstitions."

THE SQUIRREL MONKEYS

"It has, I think, now been shewn that man and the higher animals, especially the Primates, have some few instincts in common. All have the same senses, intuitions, and sensations,—similar passions, affections, and emotions, even the more complex ones, such as jealousy, suspicion, emulation, gratitude, and magnanimity; they practise deceit and are revengeful; they are sometimes susceptible to ridicule, and even have a sense of humor; they feel wonder and curiosity; they possess the same faculties of imitation, attention, deliberation, choice, memory, imagination, the association of ideas, and reason, though in very different degrees. The individuals of the same species graduate in intellect from absolute imbecility to high excellence."

Thus wrote the famous naturalist Charles Darwin, author of the theory of evolution, in his book *The Descent of Man*, published in England in 1871.

Darwin's observations form an appropriate introduction to the New World monkeys, which are pictured and described here in the following pages. For, as he says, the attributes that man shares with all the higher animals are most evidently, and in by far the greatest degree, shared with those known as the primates, of which the monkey is one.

To primates, as the name itself suggests, zoologists give the first place in the order of the animal kingdom. In doing so they recognize that it contains the most complicated and highly organized living creatures. Of the

The monkeys of the New World are found scattered throughout the vast tropical forests of the Amazon regions and on the wooded edges of the immense savannas.

eleven major groups into which the primates can be divided, only two exist exclusively in the New World and are generally included in the term New World monkeys.

A more precise name is *platyrrhini*, which comes from two Greek words meaning flat-nosed, which, broadly, is a distinguishing characteristic of all the various kinds of New World monkeys.

The Old World monkeys are also known by another name—*catarrhini*—which comes from two Greek words meaning curved-nosed, and describes the less flat and less widely separated nostrils evident in the primates of the Old World, as opposed to those of the New.

It is generally believed that the catarrhini represent a higher stage of development in the evolution of life than their New World relatives, the platyrrhini. The latter show characteristics that the former have apparently "grown out of." Yet, for all that, the platyrrhini represent a high form of life.

One of the features unique to the New World monkeys is their "fifth hand" as it is sometimes called—their prehensile, or grasping, tail, which none of the catarrhini possesses.

Yet not all of the platyrrhini are so equipped either. The squirrel monkey, one of the most common of the New World monkeys, cannot grasp or hold anything with its tail, although its tail is long.

The squirrel monkey is about ten inches in length from head to toe, and its tail is about fourteen inches long. It has a small expressive face and large eyes, and is arboreal in habit, like most of the platyrrhini.

The squirrel monkey is omnivorous in diet, eating everything, insects, fruit, and even birds.

That is, it lives and spends most of its time in bushes and trees above the ground (*arbre* is French for tree, hence arboreal = tree-living) and does not usually descend to the forest floor below.

This is a matter of security, not one of taste, for all manner of dangers are to be found on the forest floor, and the greatest safety lies in the lush leafy thick of the forest high above ground.

When the squirrel monkey does descend, it does so in great groups, all at once, to the accompaniment of much crashing and chattering. This makes its coming sound at least more fearful for others than it actually is.

The squirrel monkey is found in the tropical forests of Central and South America, ranging from Nicaragua to Bolivia and Peru. It does not usually live in the deepest, darkest parts of the forests, but prefers the sunlit edges, the river banks of the valley of

the Amazon, and the scrub woodlands that edge the great savannas.

It is omnivorous in diet, eating anything and everything—insects, spiders, small tree frogs, snails, fruit, eggs, and even birds.

It travels in troops that tend to keep close-knit, no member straying very far from any other.

There are six kinds of squirrel monkey found in South America. All are subspecies

reminiscent of the other animal from which it draws its name, it is its movement, which is quick and scampering and accomplished on "all fours." It is not like the squirrel in color, shape, or habit.

The squirrel monkey is appropriately named, for it scampers in the trees just like a park squirrel, running on all fours. It is not able, as some others of the New World monkeys are, to make use of its long, furry tail for grasping branches.

of *Saimiri sciurea*. The face is greenish white, the head dark gray or black, and the body greenish-golden in color. The greenish-golden coloring is produced by fine hairs that are yellow at the base and black at the tips. The arms and hands and feet are ruddy yellow, and the tail is gray with a black tip.

If any feature of the squirrel monkey is

More appropriately, the Tupi Indians of the Amazon called the squirrel monkey saimiri, which in their tongue means only "small monkey."

Like all monkeys the squirrel monkey is acclimated to the tropics and to the hot moist tropical forests. It does not like cold, and physically cannot stand it. The greatest

74

obstacle to keeping one in captivity is this sensitivity, and many of the thousands shipped out of the jungle die for this reason. Cold, dryness, or absence of sunlight for any prolonged period of time can prove fatal to these little monkeys.

Hardiness is less common in all the New World monkeys than it is in the Old World monkeys, some of which stand captivity reasonably well.

At about the same time that the squirrel monkey and most other monkeys of the tropical forests are settling down for the night in their various ways and protective concealments, one species is just starting out on its rounds.

*Not as large as a house cat, the douroucouli
sleeps during the day in a well-protected retreat,
coming out only at nightfall to hunt for food.*

THE DOUROUCOULIE

THE douroucouli monkey or *Aotes* is unique among the New World monkeys in being the only one that is truly nocturnal—night living.

Uniqueness in nature is not a matter of chance or caprice, as it may sometimes seem to man, but is the result of selection and specialization for survival. In the douroucouli it is the eyes that are specialized: too sensitive to be exposed for long to the full light of day, but so sensitive that even in full darkness it can see such tiny objects as insects, one of its sources of food.

This determines the douroucouli on a night course in life. When the squirrel monkey is just contentedly snuggling its furry tail around itself and going to sleep, the douroucouli is emerging from the hollow tree trunk where it has spent the day sleeping. It is starting out to look for the insect and animal fare upon which its life depends.

The sleep of the douroucouli is not profound by day, however, for there are many dangers abroad then. It must sleep half-alerted to them, so that when danger threatens, it can retreat to a safer spot.

In size the douroucouli is a little smaller than an ordinary cat. It is colored a neutral shade of brownish-gray, which blends in perfectly with the twilight and night colors of the forest in which it moves, and with the shadows among which it catches its hours of half-sleep by day.

The name *Aotes*, by which it is also known, comes from a Greek word meaning "earless," which is at least the impression one gets from its face, the ears being small and covered with hair and lying close to the head.

The douroucouli's face is dominated by a pair of large, round orange-yellow eyes, which give the animal a strangely soft and gentle expression. And, indeed, it is said to make a good pet, friendly though placid. It is prized in some areas of South America for its thoroughness in tracking down roaches and other insects in homes.

The douroucouli, when it hunts in woods at night, calls in a wide variety of voices. It can twitter and squeak like many other monkeys, and it can sound a gong-like booming noise that is loud and far-carrying and is like that of no other monkey.

For its primarily nocturnal existence, the douroucouli is equipped with large sensitive eyes.

Like the squirrel monkey, to which it is related, the douroucouli is not one of those monkeys that can use its long bushy tail for grasping.

It is, however, extremely able with the hands it does have, which possess, as do man's, thumbs that can be placed opposite to the fingers. Holding its food in one hand, the douroucouli can tear it apart easily with the other hand.

The douroucouli, in common with certain others of the platyrrhini, often bears twins. Many other monkeys have only one offspring at a time.

Another New World monkey that often bears twins is the marmoset, which also is not a "true monkey." However, in many respects it conforms more to what monkeys are thought to be than do some of the true monkeys themselves.

MARMOSETS

MARMOSETS belong to the family Callithricidae, as opposed to the true monkeys, which belong to the family Cebidae. Yet marmosets have been described by one eminent naturalist as "the most perfectly adapted of all Primates for arboreal existence."

Their movements are quick and jerky, and are carried out with such suddenness that they can disappear in the blink of an eye. This, actually, is the only defense they need against a stronger adversary with whom one may find itself suddenly confronted. Its tactic is to stare at its enemy and hope that, while the latter is trying to make up its mind how to attack, some momentary distraction may catch its eye for a second. In that second the marmoset will have leaped to new cover and safety.

Like most monkeys and near-monkeys, marmosets travel in bands—males, females and children of a family together.

The marmoset's diet is made up mainly of insects, which it obtains with characteristic quick movements.

It is one of the paradoxes of the marmoset that while being relatively limited in its facial expressions, it is thought by many to be among the platyrrhini that most closely resemble man.

It does not grimace or smirk or make faces the way many monkeys do. To convey its anger or displeasure it can only pull back its lips and bare its teeth. This is about the limit of its expressiveness and yet in composure the face of the marmoset is much more like man's than those of some of the more imitative monkeys. The marmoset has sharp pointed teeth which can easily pierce human skin. Yet as a rule it becomes a pleasant pet, friendly to those it knows, though something of a danger to strangers who approach too close.

According to Edward Bartlett, a famous naturalist who explored the Amazon animal world, the Indian women of Peru make pets of marmosets.

Marmosets were brought back to Europe from the New World in the middle of the sixteenth century and though they were not classified by naturalists for another two centuries, they almost immediately became the prized pets of the royal and the wealthy aristocrats. Perhaps the most prized and popular was the beautifully pelted silver, or black-tailed, marmoset, which takes its name from its silvery-white coat.

Marmosets are distributed over the vast regions of the equatorial forests of South America, with different species concentrated in specific areas. The silver marmoset, for example, is said to be distributed in "a marginal strip along the right bank of the Amazon between the right bank of the Tapajos and the left bank of the Tocantins."

Marmosets usually have twin offspring. Sometimes, however, they have not two but three young, and then it is not uncommon for the mother to kill one of them at birth.

The common marmoset, or ouistiti, with its long colorful tail, is one of the most perfectly adapted of all primates for an arboreal existence.

Although this may seem cruel, it is probably instinctive, and in any event a kindness to the two that survive. The survivors, being well nourished, both have a better chance of survival in the forest than any one would have had if all three had lived.

At birth the mate assists, receiving each baby as it is born, bathing it with his tongue,

and transferring it to his back, where it clings, hidden in his long hair. His services do not end there either, for he carries the children on his back, sometimes for as many as seven weeks afterwards. It is usual for the young marmoset to begin its independent acquaintance with the world at about three weeks of age, when it may climb down off its father's back and make short trips into its surroundings. But it hurries back at the first sign of danger or in response to any summons from its father.

The common marmoset (*Callithrix jacchus*) is also known by the name ouistiti,

which was given to it by the Amazon Indians. The ouistiti's mating cry is the same as its name—"uistiti-uistiti."

The Indians of the Amazon naturally saw a great deal of the many different kinds of monkeys in the tropical forests of that region, and it is not surprising that many of their myths and legends, like those of the northern Indians that dealt with deer and buffalo, concern the little primates of the New World.

The Indians tell this story of the way the monkey came to behave as it does—to utter its flute-like cries, and to live so much in the trees.

"Long, long ago the Monkey and the Tapir were friends and often spent their time together. One day they decided to take a walk in the forest. The Tapir had his flute with him, an instrument that he delighted in playing much of the time. The Monkey was envious of the Tapir's flute and he talked the Tapir into lending it to him, though the Tapir was not very happy to do so. As soon as the Monkey had it in his possession he scampered up a tree and, putting the instrument to his lips, let loose a deafening squall of sounds. After a while the Tapir asked for his flute back, but the Monkey said no, he might as well forget it, the flute was his now. This infuriated the Tapir, who swore he would kill the Monkey if he ever caught him. The Monkey heard his threat and to save himself from the Tapir's vengeance, never again came down from the trees."

Science gives a less fanciful explanation of the monkey's ways, although it agrees that it lives in the trees as a matter of security. It says the monkey's vulnerability to the more ferocious ground animals requires it to live above ground, and that its specialized limbs enable it to do so. And its voice, which is developed to a fairly high degree, is not the gift of the tapir, but grows from the need it has to keep in touch with the fellow-members of its tribe, for warning of danger.

For all their monkey-like ways, the marmosets are not considered "true monkeys," the term reserved for members of the family Cebidae. One difference is the tail, which in the marmoset is not prehensile. Another is that the marmoset has claws on all of its digits except its great toe, which has a nail. True monkeys have nails on all their toes and fingers.

Silver marmosets such as those shown here were first taken to Europe from the New World in the middle of the sixteenth century. They became the prized and costly pets of the wealthy and the royal. The marmoset is small but quick in its movements and by that quickness is often able to escape unscathed from chance and unexpected encounters with larger, more powerful animals.

The disposition of the spider monkey, friendly as a rule, contradicts the woeful expression of its face.

SPIDER MONKEYS

THE spider monkey is a true monkey. It has nails on its toes and fingers and it possesses a tail that is prehensile and in many ways more useful to it than its hands or feet.

The spider monkey's tail is its most extraordinary possession. It is longer than the monkey's body is—over two feet in length in an adult, and composed of twenty-three vertebrae, which give it suppleness and strength. It is longer and narrower than any of the monkey's other limbs and can be used to reach farther and into smaller places than can the animal's arms and legs. The monkey can hang by it, swing by it, pick fruit with it, even throw things with it.

The normal means of travel of the spider monkey is known as "brachiation"—a swinging progression from one limb or vine to the next and on to the next that is like the movement of a trapeze artist on swings.

Normally the spider monkey dwells in the topmost branches of the tall forest trees, and seldom if ever comes down to the ground.

The spider monkey travels in bands of ten, twenty, or more, often mingling with the capuchin monkey. At dawn it begins to look for food and is busiest until about ten o'clock in the morning. It feeds periodically throughout the day but not with the same intense activity with which it began at dawn.

When it walks along a limb on all fours, it carries its tail arched into an S shape. If

82

startled by something below, it will often descend to get a closer look at the intruder, emitting a barking sound that has been described as "terrier-like." It has been known to throw twigs and branches down at humans and to give other forceful signs of its displeasure at their presence.

Captivity has less dire consequences for the spider monkey than for many others, which, as a rule, do not live well in zoos or private homes. In spite of the expression of worry on its face, the spider monkey has a gentle, friendly disposition, and its constitution is relatively hardy. For this reason it is much valued as a pet.

As opposed to the female marmoset, who calls upon her mate to assist her at the birth of her young, the female spider monkey withdraws from her troop shortly before she is due to give birth, and does not return to it until two to four months have passed. Then she returns, bringing her young with her. And it is she, not the male, who carries them about, first clinging to her chest, later riding on her back. In twelve months the young spider monkey achieves its full skeletal growth, though it continues to gain weight after that time.

There are four different species of spider monkeys and four times as many subspecies, each differing from the others in some degree—in color or texture of coat, in habitat, diet, and so on.

The little spider monkey moves about by brachiation, swinging from one limb or vine to another.

THE UAKARI

A MONKEY that blushes when it is angry is the uakari, which also enjoys the distinction of being the only one of the New World monkeys to possess a short tail, a feature fairly common in the Old World monkeys.

The uakari is a cat-sized monkey with a well-developed brain and superior intelligence. Its favored habitat is among the high places of the forests, through which it travels on streets and avenues of crossing and intertwining limbs, vines, and branches.

It fears only the eagles that soar over the forest and the few snakes that venture up from the ground.

There are three species of uakari, and two of them possess the power of blushing.

The bald or white uakari, found in the Amazon region, has a pink face and skin and a coat of lank gray hair. The red uakari, found in a neighboring region, has a vermilion face, paler skin, and a coat of long reddish hair. These two will turn even redder in the face when stirred to anger. The third type of uakari, the black-headed uakari, does not.

It was probably one of the blushing uakari that the Spaniards called "mono feo" or "ugly monkey." Bald and hairless about its head, with its long coat bedraggled-looking at best, the uakari may, to human standards, seem far from beautiful.

The uakari is particularly unsuited to life in captivity, being neither very lively nor very hardy when put in a cage. The younger ones are said to be more willing to attach themselves to keepers and to adapt to zoo life, but even they are very sensitive to climate, diet, and other factors.

Although not sociable to any degree in captivity, uakaris are normally friendly in the wild, and travel and band together with others of their kind. They do develop family groups. The males are very protective of the females and will attack a person who appears to threaten them.

The normal diet of uakaris is fruit, which may include shoots, nuts, roots, bulbs. In captivity they have been found very difficult to keep properly nourished.

The red uakari (left) turns redder when it's angry, a property it shares with man. Yet anger seems far from the thoughts of the gentle-eyed one above.

CAPUCHIN MONKEYS

QUITE different from the uakari is the capuchin monkey, which, of the many New World kinds, is perhaps the most common, most captured, and most captivating to human audiences.

The capuchin is also the most intelligent of the platyrrhini, with a brain that is highly developed and large in proportion to the size of the animal itself.

This undoubtedly accounts for the capuchin's often being seen as an organ grinder's playful little assistant, a sight that once was common in Europe, and to a lesser degree in North and South America.

Such capuchins were taught to distinguish between coins of different values, to show gratitude to the givers of larger coins, and to show contempt or even abuse to the givers of pennies.

The stories that demonstrate this little monkey's intelligence are numerous. They

will sit with attention and watch a movie, showing reactions to animals appearing on the screen, such as fright at snakes.

A capuchin can be ingenious in getting to its food, one having used a short stick to dislodge a longer stick to dislodge a still longer stick that it could use to dislodge its food from a high place.

In the wild the capuchin travels in troops of from ten to fifty or more members. It does not make a home, like the douroucouli, which may return to the same resting place several days in a row, but beds down for the night wherever the end of the day may find it.

The capuchin takes its name from the Capuchin monk, whose cowl the monkey's head-coloring resembles. Although there are many species, differing from one another in color, the typical capuchin is about a foot and a half long, with a slender prehensile tail a few inches longer than that. It weighs only from two to four pounds.

It is found in Central and South America from Honduras to the northern tip of Argentina.

When food is plentiful the life of the capuchin in the forest seems remarkably easy. It rises with the sun and feeds busily for a few hours, and then spends a few more hours in various forms of relaxation. The younger ones play among themselves while the older ones sit and sun themselves and chatter to one another. This siesta-like interlude is interrupted for a few more hours of leisurely feeding and then is resumed when the heat of the day becomes oppressive.

The capuchin diet is made up of fruit, insects, birds' eggs, and even small birds.

When angered, the capuchin arches its back and spits like a cat. It can also bark like a dog. Generally its humor is good and friendly and its disposition makes it a popular pet.

Whatever it is that makes one animal friendly and another unfriendly is hard to

The capuchin monkey gets its name from the coloring around its head and shoulders, which is reminiscent in effect of the cowl and habit of the Capuchin monks. Of all the New World species, the capuchin monkey is the most intelligent, and the most widely distributed in captivity, which it survives reasonably well. And what would the organ grinders do without this nimble little companion?

say, but the capuchin is definitely among the friendlier animals and develops an apparent affection for men.

It may well have been a capuchin monkey that figures in this story, told by Charles Darwin in *The Descent of Man*.

"Several years ago a keeper at the zoological gardens showed me some deep and scarcely healed wounds on the nape of his own neck, inflicted on him . . . by a fierce baboon. The little American Monkey, who was a warm friend of this keeper, lived in the same compartment and was dreadfully afraid of the great baboon. Nevertheless, as soon as he saw his friend in peril, he rushed to the rescue, and by screams and bites so distracted the baboon that the man was able to escape, after, as the surgeon thought, running great risk to his life."

Boldness and curiosity mark the capuchin, and on occasion get it in trouble, as above, where one has mistaken a poisonous coral snake for some `less dangerous variety. In the wilds the capuchins travel in bands of from ten to fifty members, keeping up a constant chatter as they go, playing and feeding most of the day. When night comes they settle down where they are, keeping no permanent home.

SLOW ONES

Slothfulness is not a virtue among men, and the sloth, while it may be widely envied, is seldom praised. The sloth comes in for quite a bit of ridicule from man, as if its comical smile and slow way of moving were somehow its own doing.

Before one laughs, however, at the sloth or the unhurried tortoise, it would be well to remember that both are very ancient species. Their slowness has proved entirely adequate to the demands made upon them for many thousands and thousands of years. And unless man—who alone has the power to change life on earth from its natural course—intervenes, these animals will probably go on in their slow way for many thousands upon thousands of years more.

THE SLOTHS

THERE are two kinds of tree sloths, the two-toed and the three-toed. Both are found in Central and South America. They were given the name sloth because of their very slow, sluggish movements.

Unless they are disturbed, sloths spend three-quarters of the day sleeping. Normally they sleep hanging from the branch of a tree, holding on with their strong claws. The rest of the time they spend eating the leaves and buds of trees. Even their eating is done in the slowest of slow motion.

Sloths have algae, tiny microscopic plants, that grow in their long hair. During the rainy season in these animals' tropical home, the algae in the fur turn green. It is then almost impossible to see the "green" sloths among the dense vegetation of the forest. However the keen eyes of the harpy eagle can sometimes spot a sloth and this big bird then swoops down and captures the sloth in its strong talons.

Sloths are capable of protecting them-selves by slashing out at a would-be pred-

For the first three months of its life, the baby sloth clings to its mother's fur and is carried with her wherever she goes, safe as long as she is.

The strong sharp claws on its toes, with which the sloth holds onto trees and branches, are also the animal's only means of defense against predators.

ator with their strong claws. But their greatest protection probably comes from their immobility—they are simply not seen by other animals. They are regarded as inedible by most people in Central America; in South America they are eaten by some tribes of Indians.

The green tinge to the hair of the sloth is produced by minute plants called algae, which live in the hair and, during the rainy season, turn green, thus helping disguise the animal against the natural greenery of its tropical background.

It is almost impossible for the three-toed sloth to move on the ground since it cannot stand upright. The two-toed sloth is somewhat more active. If they are forced into water, sloths are good swimmers and can even swim rapidly.

Scientists who have studied the sloths in their native habitat have found that these slow animals have what seems to be the lowest body temperature of all the mammals. Their temperature may reach a low of 75°F., although the normal range for them is from 85°F. to 91°F.

The coarse hair of sloths parts in a peculiar manner, compared to that of other mammals. Apparently sloths have lived upside down for so many centuries that their hair parts on the underside of their bodies and hangs down toward their backs. Most other mammals have hair parts on their backs, with hair falling down their sides.

The mating season is the one time when sloths are seen together. Normally they live entirely alone. In captivity it is not possible to keep two females together; they bite and slash each other.

Except for a short while during the mating season, the sloth lives alone, apparently liking solitude.

The baby sloth clings to its mother's fur during the first few months of its life and is carried about in the trees hanging to her body. The two-toed sloth will actively defend her baby if she is forced to.

Sloths have lived in the world for a very long time. During the Pleistocene Epoch there were giant ground sloths living in both South and North America. They ate leaves and plants. One ground sloth was twenty feet long. In South America, remains of these ground sloths have been found in caves with man-made objects. This would indicate that these sloths became extinct fairly recently.

THE CAPYBARAS

CAPYBARAS are the largest living rodents. When they are full grown they are about three feet long and weigh as much as one hundred pounds. They look like very large guinea pigs and are indeed closely related to them.

Capybaras live in Panama and South America. They are almost always found near streams or rivers. They eat aquatic plants as well as grasses.

The capybara is a rodent, the largest rodent in the world. It is found in areas of South America.

They are gentle creatures and their only means of defense from their numerous enemies is to try to escape. Fortunately, they are excellent swimmers and can sometimes avoid a hungry jaguar or puma by taking to the water. However, once in the water they have to avoid caimans and anacondas. The Indians of the regions where the capybaras are found hunt them for food. In areas where they are hunted, the capybaras now come out to feed only at night.

They are sociable animals and seem to live in family groups of ten or more. Capybaras make contented clicking sounds when they sun themselves along the banks of streams.

During the Ice Age capybaras lived in Florida. Fossil forms of capybaras have been found which are larger than ones living today. Only one species still exists.

Capybaras seem to tame easily and are often seen in zoos.

Capybaras are never far from water, which offers them food and, when necessary, a mode of escape.

THE TURTLES

The most famous tortoises, as well as the largest, are those found in the Galapagos Islands. Individuals among these giant land tortoises have weighed four and five hundred pounds.

At one time there were great numbers of land tortoises living on the volcanic Galapagos. However during the whaling days in the South Pacific men discovered that they could be used for meat. Thousands of them were packed aboard whaling vessels and killed for food. The tortoises could go for long periods without food and water. They were slaughtered as needed to provide the crew members with fresh meat. After whaling had stopped, because of the discovery of petroleum, fishermen still continued to kill large numbers of these turtles

Turtles are cold blooded; their body temperature is regulated by the air temperature Thus they cannot survive extremes of cold or heat.

for the oil that could be secured from their bodies.

Today the Galapagos tortoises are in danger of being totally exterminated. They apparently lay very few eggs and these as well as the young turtles are destroyed by the rats, wild dogs, cats, and other animals which man has introduced into these islands. Some of them can be seen in zoos, but they have seldom bred in captivity.

The desert tortoise, found in western American deserts, is related to the Galapagos tortoise but it is much smaller, only about ten inches long. These desert tortoises, like their larger relatives, eat cacti. They are not active during the heat of the day, but rest in underground hiding places. When the temperature falls in the evening they come out to feed.

During mating season the males often have battles over the females. They try to tip each other over and one is sometimes successful. With a great deal of effort a tortoise can succeed in getting back on its feet, but in the meantime the victor has gone off with the female.

Turtles which live in a completely different environment are the sea turtles. The largest of these is the leatherback which may be six to eight feet long and weigh over a thousand pounds, although turtles of this size are rare. The green turtle, caught commercially for food, may weigh four hundred pounds.

Most sea turtles live in warm ocean waters. Their legs have become modified into flippers so that they can make rapid progress, sometimes reaching a speed of twenty miles through the water. They still need to breathe air and must come up to the surface at least every few hours.

Sea turtles return to land to lay their eggs. The female laboriously crawls up on a sandy beach and digs a hole in which she may deposit as many as one hundred eggs. Then she covers them with sand, and goes back to the sea.

The eggs hatch from one to three months later and the tiny young turtles get down to sea as fast as they can. Many young are lost to predators such as gulls, ospreys and large fish. In some regions turtle eggs are considered to be a great delicacy, and people dig them up. Because of the decreasing numbers of sea turtles, an effort is being made to protect them, and it is unlawful in many places to disturb their nests.

There are also turtles which live in fresh water. One of the most fascinating of these is the alligator snapper, which lives in the southern part of the United States. The alligator snapper may measure more than two feet in length and may weigh one hundred and fifty pounds. It spends its life almost entirely in the water; only the female comes out to lay her eggs on land.

During the mating season, the male desert tortoises fight among themselves for the females. Victory in such battles goes to the one that succeeds in tipping its opponent over on his back, as pictured above. This predicament, although difficult to recover from quickly, does not have the fatal consequences that frequently attend the battles of males of other species.

Although it is adapted to life in the water, the sea turtle must come up to the surface to breathe.

The alligator snapper has its own built-in fish lure—a projection on the front of its tongue which looks like a wiggling worm. Any fish that investigates this lure is apt to become food for the turtle.

Turtles are the oldest living order of reptiles. Their ancestors were on earth two million years ago, even before the dinosaurs, and present-day turtles have not changed very much since then. It is thought that their shell has aided their survival.

All of them lay eggs and all of them have shells. This shell, covered with horny plates in most species and with leathery skin in others, is the turtle's defense against its

enemies. Because of this heavy shell, a turtle moves slowly on land. A tortoise can travel about one quarter of a mile in an hour, if it does not decide to rest on the way. Turtles are cold-blooded, which means that their body temperature is regulated by the temperature of the air. For this reason they are not found in very cold climates, and must hibernate during the winter months in temperate regions. Those that live in hot climates cannot stay in the sun—they would die if exposed for any length of time to a temperature above 110° F.—and must hide in shaded or cool spots during the day.

Yet with luck, turtles can live to be older than most other animals. There is a record of one tortoise in captivity that lived to be one hundred and fifty years old. In the United States the word turtle is usually used to refer to those species which live largely in water; the word tortoise to those species which live entirely on land.

There are about two hundred species of turtles found in the world today.

The desert tortoise is not equipped to outfight or outrace an enemy: when danger nears, its only defense is to retract within its protective shell and wait for the situation outside to improve, a tactic that has rewarded it with great longevity.

THE CICADAS

SOUNDS of a hot summer afternoon in the country would certainly include the loud, constant, monotonous calls of the cicadas. Cicadas are perhaps the noisiest of all the insects.

Actually these penetrating calls are the mating calls of the males; most females are silent. Since the female does not have a hearing organ, scientists think she must receive the sound vibrations of the male's call. The male cicada makes his call by vibrating a membrane on a kind of sound box located on his thorax, that part of his body between his head and abdomen.

Cicadas live in their adult forms for only one short summer season. During that time they must mate and the female must lay the eggs so that there will be another generation of cicadas. When fall comes, the adults that have somehow managed to escape predators, die. Their young, however, are already in the ground.

After mating, the female hunts for a twig on a tree. Into it she ejects her eggs—often as many as two hundred. Before the end of summer these eggs have hatched and the young nymphs drop to the ground. They burrow into the earth under trees. There they remain for periods of from two to seventeen years, depending on the species. They eat sap from tree roots.

When the cicadas are full grown and it is time for them to emerge, they come to the surface of the ground. Often they build a temporary shelter of mud on top of the ground in which they live for a short while.

When they are finally ready to assume adult form, cicadas crawl up a tree trunk or a weed. When they have found a secure place, they rest for a few minutes. Then the top of their old shell begins to split open as the insect expands inside. Once the shell is split all the way from front to back, the insect begins to work its way out. First the

When the time and place are right, the cicada expands inside its shell, splitting the shell open.

head appears, then the center of the body. It stands upright with only the tip of its back still left in the old shell. Now the emerging insect lets itself fall forward. Hanging on with its legs to the old shell it pulls the back of its body out. At last it is completely free, a colorful winged creature. However it still must wait for its wings to expand and dry. Once this has occurred the cicada is an adult, ready for the last phase of its life. The whole emerging process normally takes about an hour.

A heavy rain at the time of emerging is disastrous to the cicada, as are hungry birds and other predators. Some kinds of cicadas emerge in early evening; by the next morning they are flying from tree to tree seeking a mate.

There are about fifteen hundred species of cicada in the world. Some, especially those found in the Far East, are quite large, and are used as food by people living in certain regions. For instance, the Borneo cicada is eaten by inhabitants of the Malay Peninsula. This cicada is three inches long and has a wing span of eight inches. One of the most attractive cicadas is the bright red and black blistering cicada of China. The oil cicada of Japan makes a spluttering sound resembling that made by very hot frying oil.

One of the most interesting cicadas, because of its long life span, is the periodical or seventeen-year cicada found in the forested areas of North America. In the north the nymphs live underground for

Head first it emerges from its old shell, until only its tail remains fastened inside the shell.

The cicada lets itself fall forward and, hanging on with its legs to its old shell, pulls itself free.

about sixteen years and nine months. In the south these cicadas have a thirteen-year life cycle. They do a certain amount of damage to trees by eating the sap from their roots.

Cicadas have many enemies. Small mammals eat them, birds eat them and even turtles eat them. As nymphs living underground, they often get fungus diseases. But one of the most unusual enemies of the cicadas is another insect—a wasp called a cicada killer. The female wasp stings the cicada and thus paralyzes it. Then the wasp carries the cicada, although it is larger and much heavier than she is, through the air back to a burrow she has dug in the ground. The wasp lays her egg in this burrow; when the young wasp hatches, it feeds on the captive cicada.

When it has fully emerged and its wings, unfolded, have hardened, the cicada is ready for flight.

NOISY ONES

In the natural world nothing exists without cause. This may be so because the forms that exist today have evolved through competition with rival forms. The most suitable and the most adaptable forms survived.

An application of this idea may be made in thinking about the distribution of voices of birds. Many of the ocean birds, which spend their lives mostly over water in a solitary struggle for survival, do not have voices. When they do, the voices are weak, usually used only during courtship.

Shore birds, which live between land and water, are more likely to have voices and to need them. But the real noise-makers of the bird world, the great chatterers and chirpers and singers, are the land birds. They have to defend territories and, in addition, they spend their lives surrounded by dangers of one kind or another. Their voices, and those of others, give warning of dangers, either by sudden silence or by sudden noise.

THE PARROTS

PARROTS have been popular as pets since the days of the ancient Greeks and Romans. Old prints show Christopher Columbus presenting a parrot at the court of Ferdinand and Isabella. Robinson Crusoe had a parrot on his desert island, which he brought back with him to England. There are always parrots in pirate and sailing stories. Much of their popularity is due to the ability of these birds to imitate human speech as well as other sounds when in captivity.

Parrots are found in tropical regions around the world. There are over three hundred species that range in size from about four inches to about forty inches. The smallest are the pygmy parrots of New Guinea. The largest are the macaws of Central and South America, and their total length includes their very long tails.

Macaws are often seen in zoos. They have raucous cries and are seldom still during the day. Their beaks are so strong they

In the animal order embracing parrots, there are some three hundred different species, including parakeets, macaws, and cockatoos, like the sulphur-crested cockatoo shown here.

can crack Brazil nuts with them. They do not talk as well as some of the other parrots, but they are very colorful with their green, red, yellow and blue feathers. In their native homes they are said to travel in pairs rather than in flocks, as do so many other members of the parrot family.

The best talker is supposed to be the African gray parrot. It is a handsome bird with gray feathers on its body and deep red feathers on its rather short tail. It has pale gray eyes. This is probably the bird that was a favorite with the Romans.

The best talkers of the New World parrots are the amazons from Central and South America. They are usually green with touches of red or yellow somewhere on their bodies. They have short tails and sturdy bodies. If they are trained when they are still young they can often acquire a good vocabulary of words and even whole phrases. Of course, they do not understand what they say, but merely imitate the sounds of the human who teaches them.

Many families have a small parakeet, the budgerigar, as a pet. These little birds originally come from Australia where they are often found in flocks like sparrows. They eat seeds. They do well in captivity and an occasional budgie may even learn a few words. Originally they were green birds with some yellow and blue feathers, but in captivity selective breeding has produced blue, white, and even mauve birds. In England there are special budgerigar shows each year with prizes given for color and form.

Other parrots from Australia include the handsome cockatoos. They are big birds and have crests on their heads. Like the macaws they are not especially good talkers but are kept in zoos because of their beauty. In their homeland they travel in noisy flocks.

The rainbow lorikeets, found in Australia and the East Indies, have tongues that are especially adapted for getting nectar from flowers. These birds first crush the flowers and then lap up the nectar. They travel in large flocks.

One of the most unusual parrots is the owl parrot of New Zealand. It has lost the power of flight and is now rare because so

The tongue of the rainbow lorikeet (left) *is especially adapted for getting nectar from flowers.*

The rainbow lorikeets, native to Australia, frequently travel in large flocks.

many have been killed by predatory animals brought into New Zealand by settlers. This parrot is about twenty inches long and is yellow, green, black and brown.

The owl parrot is mainly active at night in the beech forests where it lives. During the day it sleeps under the roots of trees or in cracks in rocks. It climbs trees to find its food—fruits and leaves—and when it has finished eating it spreads its wings and glides down.

These birds also nest under tree roots or among rocks. The two or three white eggs are incubated by both parents for about three weeks.

Another unusual parrot of New Zealand is the kea. These brownish-green birds live above the timberline in the mountains during the summer and nest among the rocks. However with the coming of winter the keas move down to warmer areas. After extensive sheep ranching was begun by settlers in New

Zealand, the keas discovered a new source of food in winter—the discarded remains of slaughtered sheep. They acquired such a taste for sheep fat that eventually the birds began killing live sheep. New Zealanders put a bounty on keas for some time, but finally found that the way to keep the birds from killing sheep was simply to bury re-mains of slaughtered sheep so the keas could not learn to eat meat.

New Guinea and nearby islands are the home of the tiny pigmy parrots. They have tails similar to those of woodpeckers and use them in much the same way.

Some species of pigmy parrots build their nest in the nests of termites; others nest in holes in trees. For some unknown reason it is impossible to keep pigmy parrots alive in captivity.

At one time there were parrots in the United States. They were called Carolina parakeets. Great flocks of them lived in the country east of the Rockies. Unfortunately when the country was being settled, and before the days of conservation, farmers killed large numbers of these birds because they ate the fruit on the farmers' trees. When a few birds were shot, the flock would return to see what had happened to them. It was then easy for the farmer to kill the rest of the flock. None have been seen since 1920.

Most parrots nest in holes and lay white eggs. They have strong beaks and thick tongues. They eat nuts, seeds and fruits. Some of them use their claws to hold and to bring food to their mouths, almost as if their claws were hands. Many kinds of parrots are thought to mate for life.

The little love birds, small parrots found in Asia and Africa, make perhaps the most obviously devoted mates in the bird world. When caged, they show each other constant attention and if one dies the other is said to pine away unless another mate is provided for it.

A distinguishing characteristic of the cockatoo is the crest on its head, a band of feathers that it can raise and fan forward whenever it chooses.

Although the parrot has a reputation for ability to learn to speak, in nature it imitates no voice other than its own, which is loud and unmusical.

THE GULLS

THE mewling cries of gulls soaring high in the air is a familiar sound in many coastal cities. Yet it still seems strange to see these long-winged birds circling in the air above tall buildings.

The raucous gulls are a welcome addition to harbor cities, for they are valuable scavengers. They keep the waters clean of garbage and of dead animal matter. They usually alight on the water to pick up their food, but will sometimes swoop down and pick up food on the wing. If several gulls see the same piece of food at the same time, there may be a noisy fight about it.

Some gulls also eat clams and other shell fish. However, they are not able to open the shells with their beaks, so they have devised an ingenious method of getting the creatures which live inside. The birds pick up the clams in their beaks and fly over a beach, or a concrete road or even a parking lot, and drop the clam. The shell breaks and the gull swoops down and eats the clam.

Most gulls are seen near shore. They will follow ships for a short distance to see if garbage might be discarded, but will turn back before they are too far out to sea. Only the kittiwake, one of the smaller gulls, is known to travel long distances at sea. It seems to follow the fishing fleets. Kittiwakes banded in England have been found later in Newfoundland on the North American coast.

Gulls are sociable birds and nest in colonies with other gulls and even with other sea birds such as terns, puffins and cormorants. However, if a nest is left unattended in such colonies, the gulls will eat the eggs and young of the other birds. Gulls usually lay two or three brown speckled eggs in a nest of seaweed on an isolated beach or on an uninhabited small rocky island. The young

are covered with mottled brown down and are able to run about from the time they hatch, but stay near the nesting site for a month or more. If the baby gulls make the mistake of wandering into a neighboring gull's nest, they are apt to be killed.

It takes the larger species of gulls about three years to get their adult gray and white, black and white, or all white plumage.

Before that time they have flecked brown and white feathers and look very different from adult birds. With each succeeding year their plumage gets lighter in color, so that it is possible to tell the approximate age of young birds.

If gulls can stay alive during the first year of their lives, they often live for many years. There is a record of one banded herring gull

Perhaps the most commonly seen gull is the herring gull. It is a large gull, measuring about twenty-six inches in length. It has a gray back and black wing tips.

Along the West Coast of the United States the common gull is the California gull. It looks rather like a small herring gull but it has greenish legs, instead of pinkish. The California gull is immortalized by a monument in Salt Lake City. When the Mormons first settled in Utah, a plague of crickets descended on their crops. These insects were eaten by flocks of California gulls, and

Nesting swallow-tailed gulls may be found in the Galapagos at almost any time of the year. A single egg is laid in a depression among the rocks.

that lived in the wild for twenty-eight years.

There are forty-three species of gulls in the world and they range in size from eleven inches to thirty-two inches. The great black-backed gull is one of the largest, as is the nearly white glaucous gull. Both species are found in the northern hemisphere.

enough of the crop was saved to see the Mormons through the next year. To show their gratitude the Mormons had a statue made of the California gull.

Another species of gulls which may be found far inland from the sea is the small black-headed Franklin gull. During the summer months it lives in the interior parts of the United States, nesting in marsh areas. At the time of plowing, Franklin gulls often follow the plow, scratching up uncovered insects. However, in the fall these gulls migrate south and spend the winter in salt water along the Gulf Coast.

Two gulls nest on the Galapagos Islands, the swallow-tailed and the dusky. However, during the time when it is not nesting, the swallow-tailed gull makes a long trip over the sea to the coasts of Ecuador and Peru; the dusky gull, on the other hand, is seldom

This bird nests on many of the Galapagos Islands and possibly on other small islands to the north. A single egg is laid from which hatches a downy chick. The young gulls are sometimes eaten by the Galapagos hawks.

The dusky gull is a grayish-brown bird. Like many other animals of the Galapagos it is exceedingly friendly to and curious about men who come to these islands.

Dusky gulls nest all through the year but are very secretive about their nesting sites. Their main food seems to be small crustaceans.

found farther away from islands near the Galapagos.

The swallow-tailed gull is the only gull which has a forked tail. A white triangle can be seen in its long gray wings when the gull is in flight. It eats squid and fish that swim near the surface of the water.

A frequent sight at the seashore, especially near dunes where they nest, are groups of great black-backed gulls with a few darker young among them.

PEACEFUL ONES

The difference between a wolf and a dog is partly one of domestication: over years of breeding, dogs have been developed which, in an environment with humans, do not have to kill for their food. Out of disuse, their ferocity, once no doubt equal to the wolf's, lies dormant and unexercised.

The natural way of some animals, however, never requires them to be ferocious. This is particularly true of those animals that eat plants, which they hardly need fight to conquer. Female sheep and cows, for example, probably never were much given to fighting, though undoubtedly breeds developed in captivity have lessened whatever ferocity they once possessed.

THE BOOBIES

It is not really known exactly why boobies were given that name by sailors who first saw them and may have visited their nesting colonies on tropical islands. The sailors may have thought that the birds were "boobies" because they were so trusting. Since boobies nest, for the most part, on small uninhabited islands, they were unacquainted with men and permitted the sailors to approach without showing any signs of the fear that wild animals normally show at the approach of men.

Regardless of the reason, the six species of gannets living in tropical waters have retained the common name of booby.

Boobies are relatively large sea birds. They are white and black or white and brown, depending on the species. The colorful parts of their bodies are those covered by naked skin rather than feathers. For instance there are the blue-footed boobies,

the blue-faced boobies, and the red-footed boobies. But these colors may change between the breeding and the non-breeding seasons.

Most boobies tend to nest in colonies. It is thought that those living below the equator nest between October and April, although being tropical birds, they may also have no definite nesting season. The adult males usually arrive at the future nesting sites first and pick a territory. The females soon follow, and each accepts a particular male as her mate. Most boobies mate for life and the pair bond is strong.

Boobies generally nest on the ground, although a few species build crude nests in trees. A common display among them is for the male to offer the female a twig or pebble for the nest. Other ceremonies may include mutual neck preening and an uptilting of heads. Their cries on the nesting grounds

The blue-footed booby nests from Baja California south to Peru and on the Galapagos Islands. The young are covered with white down.

are described as trumpeting and whistling. Most boobies raise only one young each season, although they may lay two or more eggs. Both the female and the male incubate the eggs and care for the young birds. The young booby is almost nude when it first comes out of the egg, but within a short time it is covered with white down. Both parents feed their offspring, at first with regurgitated food and later with small whole fish.

During the first days of its life the young

The young boobies wander far from their nesting sites and may travel thousands of miles. During each molt their feathers become closer to the colors of the adult plumage. Finally, after from three to five years they return to their ancestral grounds to mate.

Boobies are expert fishers. They fly above the water until they sight a fish. Then with wings closed or half closed, they dive often from heights of fifty feet or more. They can swim underwater, using both their wings

Boobies at sea fly ahead of a ship looking for the flying fish that glide and skitter off the bow wave.

booby is shielded from the hot tropical sun by its brooding parents. Later, however, the parents leave it for ever-increasing periods of time. Soon the young bird loses its down, and in about four to six months its first plumage of mottled brown and white feathers comes in. At last it is ready to take off to sea and fish for itself.

and feet. They eat the fish underwater, rather than returning to shore with it.

Boobies tend to feed in small flocks in the early morning and in the late afternoon. During bright moonlit nights they may fly all night. They are often harassed by frigatebirds which make them regurgitate the fish they have been lucky enough to catch.

The black-browed albatross builds a tall nest, but some other species lay their eggs on bare ground.

THE ALBATROSSES

Albatrosses are truly birds of the sea; only when they nest do they come to land. Gliding on long, pointed wings, albatrosses ride the winds for hours and may travel several hundred miles a day. At night they rest on the surface of the sea, often feeding on squid and other small ocean animals during that time.

Albatrosses have followed ships in southern waters since the early days of exploration in the seventeenth century. Sailors call the larger species gooney birds and the smaller ones mollymawks. Sometimes an albatross will accidentally land on the deck of a ship and for a time be unable to take flight. If it is approached by a man, it will

Of the fourteen species of albatrosses in the world, nine live entirely within the southern hemisphere. There they are found chiefly in the region between 30° and 60° south latitude where there are strong prevailing west winds. Albatrosses depend on winds not only to help them take off but also for sustained flight. On calm days these big birds are almost unable to take off and usually stay on the surface of the water.

disgorge a jet of yellow oil from its mouth, apparently in an attempt to defend itself.

Most albatrosses nest on remote islands, usually in colonies. The males arrive first and begin occupying their territories. When the first females come, each is surrounded by several male birds. The males in turn, bow and spread their wings. After all have finished, the female selects her mate and goes off to the nesting site with him. Then

118

the paired birds begin their courtship displays, nibbling at each other's feathers, throwing their heads up, stretching out their wings and occasionally braying.

Nests are used year after year although not by the same pairs. Some species build nests of mud and grasses on the ground. The male brings the material in his beak to the female and she arranges it into a small cone-shaped nest. Eventually she lays a single white egg which both parents take

When they are fully mature, they join the other breeding albatrosses on islands.

The wandering albatross is the largest. It has an eleven-foot wing spread and is about four feet long.

One of the most common albatrosses of the southern hemisphere is the black-browed albatross, which has a wing spread of seven and a half feet. These birds nest on many islands, including the Falklands. Sealers and whalers used to raid their nests

The black-browed albatross does not often come to land, and may, between landing on land once and landing once again, soar over thousands of miles of vacant ocean. It may even travel completely around the globe out of sight of land, which it comes to only to mate and to raise its young.

turns incubating for seventy to eighty days depending on the species.

When the young albatross finally hatches, it is covered with down. It is fed by its father and mother for a long period; for example, young of the largest albatrosses stay in the nest for eight months. Only then are they fully feathered and able to fly.

Once the young birds leave the nest they spend their next few years on the ocean.

for eggs, as they did many other colonies of nesting albatrosses.

Most albatrosses are gray and white or black and white, but two species, the sooty and light-mantled sooty, are brownish-gray. The sooties do not nest in colonies but in pairs in hidden spots on cliffs on subantarctic islands.

The Laysan and the black-footed albatrosses nest on islands in the Pacific.

THE HARES

In early spring the European male hares can be seen doing all kinds of strange antics —leaping in the air, tumbling about on the ground, and fighting among themselves.

From the description "as mad as a March hare" it is obvious that this behavior is customary at the beginning of the hare's mating season.

Hares belong to the same family as rabbits. Hares, however, are usually larger than rabbits. Their young are born with fur and with their eyes open. Rabbits are born naked and with their eyes closed.

Hares and rabbits are very important in the balance of nature. They are food for thousands of predators, foxes, owls, hawks, snakes, weasels, coyotes, bobcats and many others. Consequently the hares are in constant danger, and only a small percentage of them live for longer than a year. They

have no means of defense, although a mother hare will try to fight to protect her young. They can run very fast and sometimes escape from enemies in this way. The jackrabbit of western United States (which is really a hare) has been clocked at a speed of forty miles an hour. It can make twenty-foot leaps, too. Jackrabbits are perhaps the fastest of all the hares.

During the day hares spend most of their time resting in "forms" on their territory. These "forms" are just favorite sitting places where the hare feels protected—in a log, or a brush pile, or sometimes in the open. In the evening and during the night the hares feed. They are vegetarians and will eat almost all kinds of plants.

The colors of the varying hare change with the seasons, from white in winter to brown in summer.

One of the most interesting hares of North America is the varying hare. It is also called the snowshoe rabbit because of its furred feet, with which it can walk easily on snow. During the winter this hare has thick white fur. Only its ear tips are black. However in the spring it begins shedding its white fur, and its brown summer coat starts coming in. By midsummer it is completely brown. In the fall it begins turning white again. These

121

color changes make it much harder for its enemies to see the varying hare in its natural habitat.

Varying hares mate in early spring and the young are born in about a month. The average size of the litter is four. The mother does not prepare a nest for them. During the day she stays near them, but she nurses them only at night. Within a few weeks they are eating grass, and are weaned when they are about a month old. They mate for the first time when they are a year old. Varying hares may weigh as much as four pounds and be as long as eighteen inches.

Another hare which changes color with the seasons is the large arctic hare. It may weigh up to twelve pounds in Alaska, where the largest ones are found. Arctic hares provide food for many of the animals of the Arctic, including the bears, the snowy owls and the foxes, as well as for the Eskimos.

The vivid plumage of the adult golden-eye is just a promise in the mottled down of the duckling.

THE GOLDENEYES

GOLDENEYES are diving ducks which nest in holes in trees, usually near a fresh-water pond or lake. The females lay from eight to twelve eggs in the nest and cover them with down. When the ducklings hatch, they remain in the nest for about two days. Then they jump down from the tree and follow their mother to water where they can feed.

The common goldeneyes are found throughout the world in the northern hemisphere. They nest as far north as the tree line in the summer, but spend the winter in coastal waters or in fresh water that is not cold enough to be frozen.

They are handsome ducks. The male weighs about two and a half pounds. He has a dark green head with a distinctive white face patch and yellow eyes. In flight and when he is sitting on the water much of his body appears white; he has dark wings, a dark tail and dark stripes down his back. The female is smaller and is grayish-white with a brown head. She has no face patch.

The goldeneyes fly as fast as fifty miles an hour and their wings make a loud whistling sound. For this reason they are sometimes called "whistlers."

They dive for their food—crayfish, water insects, mussels, and other shellfish.

Another goldeneye found in the western part of North America, as well as in a few isolated spots on the eastern coast, is Barrow's goldeneye. It looks much like the common goldeneye, but the male has a dark purplish head and a crescent-shaped white face patch. These western birds nest along streams high in the Rocky Mountains. They, too, build their nests in holes in trees.

The curiously humped tapir is much like its Pliocene ancestors.

THE TAPIRS

At one time there were many tapirs living in the world. Fossils of them have been found in southern United States as well as in Europe.

The four species of these mammals which exist in limited numbers today have changed very little from their ancestors that lived in the Pliocene Period. They are about the size of a large hog and weigh about five hundred pounds. They have long snouts. Their legs are short and they have three toes on each hind foot and four on each front foot. They eat water plants or plants that grow near water. Tapirs are excellent swimmers and during the day often stay near rivers or lakes. At night they may venture out onto land, always trying to avoid, however, their greatest enemy, the jaguar.

They are killed for food by some Indian tribes.

Most kinds of adult tapirs have very short hair. The young animals look quite different from the adults. Until they are about six months old, they have spots and stripes on their hair.

The Baird's tapir lives in the forests of Central America. The Brazilian tapir is found in the Amazon region and the hairy tapir lives in the Andes Mountains of South America. The only other species of tapir in the world is found in parts of southeastern Asia. It has black and white hair; the tapirs of the Americas are brown.

Because of the odd number of their toes, tapirs have been placed in the same order as horses and rhinoceroses.

MYSTERIOUS ONES

First as a hunter, then as an explorer, and most recently as a naturalist and scientist, man has sought to penetrate the unknown regions of the earth. However, his curiosity, his most distinguished possession, is, against the measure of time that tells the age of the world, still in its infancy. And though man's curiosity, with increasing precision has raised more and more pertinent questions, there is still much in nature that he does not understand.

What can be said, for example, about the origin of life, or what life is, even? Or, on a lesser level, how can we explain why the jabiru makes its nest where it does? Between heaven and earth, much remains mysterious, much still to be known.

THE JAGUARUNDI

SOMETIMES the fur of this small cat is gray and sometimes it is reddish-brown. People thought that these were two different animals and called the gray cat the jaguarundi and the reddish cat the eyra. Eventually scientists found that both cats were the same, regardless of the color of their fur. Sometimes a reddish-brown female will have gray kittens in her litter, as well as kittens of her own color.

The jaguarundi lives in Central and South America. A few may even be found in the southwestern part of the United States. It is small for a wild cat, about three and a half feet long, with a small head, a long tail, and short legs. It looks more like a weasel or otter than it does like a cat. As a matter of fact in parts of Mexico it is called the otter-cat, not only because of its appearance but also because it is an excellent swimmer.

Regardless of whether it lives in the dry deserts or in tropical forests, the jaguarundi preys on birds and small animals such as rabbits, rats and mice. Like most members of the cat family, the jaguarundi climbs trees readily. It seems to hunt during the day if it lives in an uninhabited region; otherwise it hunts at night.

The jaguarundi is a secretive animal and not very much is known about its life in the wild. It lives in much of the same area as the ocelot, and possibly has much the same food habits as its spotted relative.

The jaguarundi, three feet long and weasel-like, is a relative of the ocelot and inhabits much the same regions, preying on birds and small animals.

Noiseless in flight, hunting only by sound, the barn owl is rightly called a flying mousetrap.

THE BARN OWLS

BARN owls have been called "feathered flying mousetraps," which is a good description of them since they eat mice and rats almost exclusively. For this reason, barn owls are especially valuable to farmers. Of all the owls these are the most apt to take up living quarters in man-made dwellings such as barns, church belfries, and abandoned houses. Because of their weird calls they have given many an old building a reputation of being haunted.

Barn owls have the most extensive range of all the owls in the world. They are found in every country except New Zealand and certain islands in the Pacific Ocean. There are nine or ten species of barn owls. They vary in color from the black ones of New Guinea to the familiar tan and white birds of North America.

Barn owls mate for life or at least for long periods of time. In the northern hemisphere the females lay from five to seven eggs very early in the spring. The eggs hatch in about a month. The young birds are fed mainly on rodents and, like their parents, cough up pellets of the undigestible parts such as fur and bones. The young owls are able to fly in two months.

Barn owls are rather large birds, adults measuring from twelve to nineteen inches in length. Adults do not migrate but remain in the same region winter and summer.

They catch their prey by sound, not by sight, and are able to hunt successfully in total darkness. Their heart-shaped faces seem to serve as a kind of screen to help them pick up the slightest sound when they are hunting.

126

THE TASMANIAN DEVIL

TASMANIA is an island about the size of Ireland, one hundred and fifty miles off the southern coast of Australia. It was discovered by the Dutch explorer Abel Tasman in 1642.

In Tasmania there are low mountains, forests, swift rivers, and lakes. The eastern part of the island has areas of grassland. Settlers came to Tasmania from Australia in the nineteenth century and began farming in suitable parts of the island. Today about three hundred thousand people live on the island and it is part of the Commonwealth of Australia.

There are two unusual mammals living in Tasmania which are not found anywhere else in the world. One is called the Tasmanian devil; the other is the Tasmanian wolf. They are marsupials, or pouched mammals, as are many of the Australian mammals. Unfortunately so many of them were killed by the early settlers that they are rarely seen in their native home.

The Tasmanian devil may have been called that by the people who first came to live on the island because the little animal's fur is black with white spots. Or, it may possibly have been so named because of its angry expression when cornered.

The head and shoulders of the Tasmanian devil are proportionately larger than the rest of its body and are strong enough to enable the animal to kill creatures larger than itself. It has short legs, and walks with the same swinging gait that a bear does. It is about three feet long.

The relatively large head and shoulders of the Tasmanian devil enable it to overcome bigger animals.

The Tasmanian devil is a nocturnal animal, sleeping by day, hunting by night, and, like many other animals of that part of the world, a marsupial, carrying its young in a pouch.

The Tasmanian devil makes its home along rivers. It eats birds, lizards, snakes, frogs, rodents, and large insects. And, because it sometimes raided their chicken yards, it was often killed by farmers.

These animals mate in early spring and the young are born several months later. There are usually four babies which the mother carries about in her pouch. When they get too big to fit in the pouch, the mother builds a nest for them, in which they live until they are ready to go out on their own.

The Tasmanian devil generally hunts at night and sleeps during the day, often curled up in a hollow log. Its cries have been described as being whines and snarls.

The Tasmanian wolf, the other marsupial unique to this island, looks like a dog with brown stripes running across its back.

It eats small mammals, even wallabies which are bigger than itself. Early settlers killed Tasmanian wolves in large numbers because these animals not only killed chickens but also sheep. Now the few remaining Tasmanian wolves live only in the

Native to the oceanic island of Tasmania, this little animal, the Tasmanian devil, was hunted almost off the face of the earth by the early settlers of the island, who feared it.

wildest hill regions, if any still exist. They hunt at night and sleep during the day.

The female Tasmanian wolf has four young at a time. She carries them in her pouch until they are too big for it; then she hides them in a den. Her pouch, unlike the kangaroos', opens to the back.

Scientists believe that at one time both the Tasmanian devil and the Tasmanian wolf also lived on the continent of Australia along with the many other marsupial animals found there. Marsupials are considered to be among the more primitive of present-day mammals. Their young are in an early stage of development when they are born and must continue their further development within the mother's pouch. Most other mammals give birth to young which are much more advanced in growth than the marsupial babies.

129

THE WOMBATS

The gentle little wombats are sometimes called the "badgers of Australia." However they are totally unlike the tenacious, carnivorous badgers in almost every respect. The only habit the wombats and the badgers share is that of digging burrows in the ground.

The wombat uses its sharp claws to dig a long and rather large burrow in the earth.

The wombat is a marsupial. The female has one baby at a time and the young wombat passes the first few months of its life safe in its mother's pouch.

There are two species of wombats in Australia. One has coarse grayish-black or yellowish-brown fur and a bare nose. The other has soft gray fur which extends over its nose.

The wombat is another marsupial, like the kangaroo, and lives only in Australia and Tasmania.

During the day the wombat rests in its burrow. At night it comes out to hunt for its food. It eats only grasses, tree bark and roots.

The wombat looks rather like an outsized guinea pig. It has only a tiny tail and short legs and its whole appearance is round. The average wombat is about three and a half feet long. Some may weigh as much as eighty pounds.

At one time in the long distant past a wombat the size of a large bear lived in Australia. Scientists know this because they have found fossil remains of this wombat.

The pirarucu, found in rivers of South America, is one of the world's largest fresh-water fish.

THE PIRARUCU

PIRARUCU are fresh-water fish found in the Amazon and other rivers of northern South America. They are among the largest fresh-water fish in the world. A big pirarucu may weigh two hundred pounds and be seven feet long.

Their name comes from the Portuguese "pira" meaning fish, and "rucu" meaning red. Actually their large scales are gray and are only bordered with red. Their scientific name is *Arapaima gigas*.

Pirarucu are an important food fish for the people of South America. Indian tribes have caught them for centuries, shooting them with a bow and arrow, or else harpooning them. Then they preserve the fish by drying the flesh in the sun so that it can be used for food at a later date.

Not only human fishermen go after the pirarucu—the powerful jaguar may be suc-cessful in catching one of these big fish.

Like many fish living in fresh water in which there is a great deal of decaying vegetation, the pirarucu come to the surface to breathe air. They would die if they were forced to remain under water for any length of time. When they expel the air they make a kind of burping sound that can be heard for almost a mile.

The pirarucu are among the rare fishes that not only make a kind of nest but also take care of their eggs and the babies which hatch from them.

The pirarucu and other fresh-water fish found in northern South America are almost all totally unlike those found in North America. Strangely enough, these South American fish seem to be related to fish found in Africa, and even to those of north-ern Australia.

131

THE FRIGATEBIRDS

FRIGATEBIRDS get part of their food by pirate-like actions. They soar high above the tropical oceans until they see a booby, gull or pelican returning from a successful fishing trip. Then the frigatebirds start chasing their intended victim, even pulling at its wings, tail, or legs. Often the pursued bird will regurgitate the fish it has recently eaten. The frigatebird then swoops down and picks up the fish before it hits the water.

Frigatebirds get the rest of their food by catching it themselves from the surface of the water. Their feathers are not waterproof, as are those of most other birds which catch fish, so the frigatebirds cannot dive or land on the water. Their food includes only those fish which come to the surface—herring, flying fish, jellyfish—which the birds catch by dipping their long hooked beaks into the water.

There are five species of frigatebirds found in tropical waters around the world. The one commonly seen on the southern Atlantic and Pacific coasts of the United States is the magnificent frigatebird. It also breeds in the Galapagos Islands, as well as on small, isolated islands off the coasts of Central and South America.

After forty days and forty nights, during which time both parents by turns incubate the egg, the frigatebird chick hatches and in a few days its naked skin is covered with a soft white down.

132

The magnificent frigatebirds are more than a yard long with a seven-foot wingspan. Females are slightly larger than the males. The females have white breasts while the males are all iridescent black. In both the male and female the wings are pointed and they have long forked tails.

Frigatebirds are wonderfully equipped for flight. Their pectoral, or flight, muscles weigh as much as their plumage. Together, muscles and feathers make up about half of total body weight. The bones of their skeletons are hollow, so the whole skeleton accounts for only about one-eighth of the total body weight, which averages about three and a half pounds.

North of the equator, frigatebirds nest from December to May; frigatebirds which live in the trade winds areas nest during the dry season.

The males are first to arrive at the breeding sites, which are on small uninhabited islands. Their throat pouches, or gular sacs, become crimson, and are blown up to full size. During other times of the year these pouches are deflated and are flesh-colored.

The male picks out a place to build the nest—in a mangrove tree, or in sea grape, or sometimes on a cliff. The males even start the nests, using twigs they have broken off while on the wing.

When the females arrive at the colony, the pairs begin forming. The females usually have to get the rest of the twigs for the nest because the males have to stay on the nest to keep it from being dismantled by neighboring birds. Nesting colonies of frigatebirds may also contain pelicans, gulls, boobies and cormorants. Twigs are not always easy to get, and a great deal of stealing from other nests takes place.

Normally frigatebirds are silent, but in the breeding colony they clack their bills and make clucking sounds.

The female lays a single egg which is incubated by both parents for about forty days. The baby is naked when it first hatches, but within a few days is covered with white down. It may be fed by its

parents for as long as eight months before it is entirely on its own. The young birds have white feathers on their heads. They do not get their adult plumage for about four years.

At the end of the breeding period the colony scatters. They may fly far from the nesting place, but are seldom beyond the sight of land. At night they roost in groups in low trees on islands.

The great frigatebird, which is as large as the magnificent, is found in the South Atlantic, in the Pacific, and in the Indian oceans. It also nests on the Galapagos Islands. The great frigatebird looks much like the magnificent but has brown bands in its wings. The females have red rings around their eyes. The female magnificent frigatebirds have blue eye rings.

The frigatebird has the typically sharp and hook-shaped beak found in other fish-eating birds.

The Polynesians used to put up special perches for these birds in their villages. Then they would tame the frigatebirds by feeding them fish. Eventually the islanders would tie reed cylinders to the birds' wings at night while the birds were sleeping. In the cylinders they placed a message or a small gift such as a shell fish hook. When the birds took a flight, they would often drop down on perches on other islands, and the residents of those islands would remove the message or present from the cylinders.

The three other species are the Ascension Island frigatebirds, the Christmas Island frigatebirds and the lesser frigatebirds. The lesser are the smallest species—they are thirty-two inches long.

Frigatebirds are sometimes called man-o'-war birds, a name probably given them because of their resemblance, when flying, to the graceful frigate, a fast sailing ship which was often used in warfare.

It may be as long as four years before the young frigatebird acquires the lustrous black plumage of the adult, though it flies long before then.

THE JABIRUS AND WOOD STORKS

In the wet open marshlands of Central and South America it is possible to see a tall white bird searching for frogs and insects. As this bird stalks on long black legs through the tall marsh grasses, it keeps its foot-long, thick black bill partially open so it can capture its prey quickly.

There are no feathers on the bird's head and neck. The skin on these parts of its body is black or dark gray except for the lower part of the neck, which is orange-red. The bird can distend, or puff out, the lower part of its neck so that its neck becomes larger than its head.

This big bird is a jabiru, a New World stork. There are seventeen species of storks in the world today. The most familiar is the white stork of Europe, used so often as a symbol of human maternity. Only one stork is found in the United States—the wood stork of Florida and the Gulf Coast. It also lives in South America.

Both the jabiru and the wood stork are birds of the wilderness, and never nest in towns as do the European white storks. The jabirus build their huge heavy nests atop tall trees. They may use the same nest for several years and keep adding material to it. One such jabiru nest measured eight feet across.

Two or three grayish white eggs are laid in the nest and both the male and female take turns incubating them. Soon after the babies hatch they are covered with soft white down. Their first feathers are grayish or brownish. It takes a little more than four months before the young jabiru can fly and is therefore ready to leave the nest.

The jabirus do not nest in colonies, but the wood storks do. In Florida swamps there may be several thousand nesting wood storks in one colony. The nests are often built in bald cypress trees.

Like all storks, the adult black and white wood storks are voiceless. They do clatter their heavy bills, however, and occasionally hiss or grunt. Baby storks are able to make a begging call when their parents return to the nest to feed them.

The jabiru has a wingspread of seven feet; the wood stork has a wingspread of about five feet. They are expert gliders and may often be seen circling high in the air, riding on thermals. Since they are heavy birds—a wood stork may weigh seven pounds—their ability to glide on up-drafts helps them to save energy when in flight. They fly with neck and feet outstretched in typical stork-like fashion.

Storks have been in the world for a long time—fossil remains from fifty million years ago have been found. In recent years their numbers have been decreasing. Apparently this decrease is due to the increase of human population and the drainage of swamp areas for building and development. Certain nesting colonies of wood storks in the United States are now being given special protection by conservation organizations.

The jabiru is a New World stork, ranging from southern Mexico to Argentina. Jabiru is the Mexican name for the bird, which feeds on the fish and amphibians of tropical swamps. It does not nest in cities, as the white stork does, preferring the wilds and the tops of trees. It adds to the nest each year; one jabiru nest found measured eight feet in diameter.

THE TAYRAS

The tayra is a nocturnal animal, in shape much resembling weasels and mink, with a long sleek body and relatively short legs. But the tayra is larger, three feet in length, and its fur is black and does not change during the year.

WHEN night falls in the tropical forests the tayras, tree weasels of South America, wake up and begin their search for food. They often hunt in family packs or in pairs. They eat almost anything they can find, from small animals to fruit. Since they are excellent climbers they also raid birds' nests for eggs. Tayras are active animals and have to spend most of their waking hours getting the food necessary for their energy requirements. During the day they rest in some safe, hidden spot.

Tayras are related to weasels, martens, and mink. They look rather like these important fur-bearing animals, having the same type of long body and short legs. However the tayras are about three feet long— twice or three times the size of a weasel. Unlike the weasels of the north that change color from brown to white with the coming of winter snows, the tayras have black fur throughout the year. Their heads are brown or light gray; their long tails are rather bushy.

Tayras can be seen in some zoos. They adjust reasonably well to life in a zoo environment, but thus far none have ever bred in captivity.

Another member of the weasel family which lives in South America is the grison. It is smaller than the tayras and has gray fur. The grison also does most of its hunting at night and sleeps during the day.

Tayras are now found only in Central and South America, but scientists think they may have originally been a North American species which gradually migrated south sometime during the past million years.

THE PECCARIES

PECCARIES are the native wild pigs of the Americas. They differ in several ways from the wild pigs found in the rest of the world, so scientists have classified them in their own special family.

There are only two species, the collared peccary and the white-lipped peccary. Both are found in Central and South America, and the collared peccary exists in small numbers in parts of southwestern United States as well.

Peccaries are rather small as pigs go. Their average adult length is about three feet and their weight between forty and forty-five pounds. The white-lipped peccary tends to be somewhat larger than the collared peccary.

One of the most unusual features of these pigs is a musk gland that is located on their backs a few inches from their very short tails. From this gland is secreted a liquid generally regarded as having an unpleasant odor. Apparently the peccaries use it in several ways: as a defense measure much as skunks use their scent; as a means of defining their territory by rubbing their backs against various trees and rocks in the vicinity of their home; and finally, as a signal they give to the rest of the peccaries that danger is present.

Peccaries are social animals and travel in small bands of from ten to forty. They sometimes even hunt in groups, and if one sights a rattlesnake or an ocelot—two special dangers—the others will surround the enemy and either help kill it, or at least put it to flight.

They feed early in the morning and late in the afternoon. During the day they rest in hidden spots, sometimes in a fallen log or in dens in the rocks. Although peccaries eat mainly vegetable foods, such as cacti, nuts, fruits, and roots which they dig out of the ground with their snouts, they will

The pig-like peccaries are social animals in nature, traveling together in bands of from ten to forty members, and resting as a group at night.

also eat small animals, snakes and the eggs of birds and turtles.

Their coarse hair is blackish-gray or grizzled. The collared peccary can be recognized by the white or yellowish hair around its neck; the white-lipped peccary has a white area on its face. The young pigs are yellowish or reddish-brown.

As far as is known, peccaries mate during any season of the year. The usual litter is two. The mother and her babies may appear together within a few days after birth, although at night they probably sleep in their nest in a den for some time. In a month or so they join their peccary band.

The number of these wild pigs has decreased greatly in the past century. Their most formidable enemy has been man and his gun. In the southwestern part of United

Peccaries feed early in the morning and late in the afternoon, mainly on vegetable foods, such as cacti, fruit, and edible shoots and roots.

States, farmers killed the peccaries because they sometimes destroyed crops. In tropical forests and in the mountainous areas of Central and South America they are thought to be still plentiful.

Many tales have been told of the fierceness of peccaries when attacked. Actually they are rather shy creatures and would prefer to run rather than to fight. Their natural enemies are mainly the big cats— jaguars, bobcats, and ocelots, although when they are in bands, they seem to be safe from these.

The name "peccary" comes from one of the South American Indian languages and means "a creature which makes many paths in the woods." Peccaries are also called javelina in Mexico.

The wild pigs of the Old World differ from peccaries in several ways. Their tusks curve upward or outward instead of downward. They do not have musk glands on their backs as do the peccaries. They also have small outer hooves on their hind feet which the peccaries lack.

The wild boar of Europe and Asia is the biggest wild pig in the world. Adults may be as long as four and a half feet and weigh three hundred and fifty pounds. They travel in small bands and are usually found in forests.

Females have two litters a year with as many as six pigs in each litter. The young have dark stripes down their backs. Adults have a brownish-gray coat of bristles, although there is a great deal of color variation among them, depending on the region or on the country in which they are found.

Until fairly recent times a wild boar hunt was a popular though dangerous sport in Europe. The hunting party consisted of a pack of dogs and men on horseback. The boar was killed with spears or knives. The old English custom of killing a wild boar and serving its head at Christmas dinner dates back to pagan times when the boar was a sacrificial animal.

There are three wild pigs found in Africa, the bush pig, the forest hog, and the wart hog. The bush pig lives south of the Sahara and has tufts on its ears. The seldom-seen forest hog is found in deep forests of Central Africa. The wart hog, regarded by men as one of the ugliest of animals, lives on the African plains.

Peccaries, which once were common throughout southwestern United States, were extensively hunted because of the crop damage they inflicted.

THE PTARMIGAN

PTARMIGAN are small grouse. Most of them live in the Arctic, on the tundra near the Arctic, and near the snowline on high mountains.

Scientists are not able to agree on the number of species of ptarmigan; some say there are three; others say there are four. The questionable species is a red grouse found on the moors of Scotland, England, and Ireland. Unlike that of other ptarmigan, the plumage of the red grouse does not change color in winter. But, because the Gulf Stream passes near the countries where it lives, the climate is temperate and it does not often snow. Therefore, some ornithologists think that the red grouse is actually a willow ptarmigan which does not change color. At any rate the red grouse is one of the most famous European game birds. It nests on the moors and lays from eight to ten eggs. It eats heather and other plants.

The willow ptarmigan is the largest species, adults being from fifteen to seventeen inches long and weighing about a pound.

The extra feathering that comes out on the feet of the ptarmigan in wintertime acts as a natural snowshoe, spreading the weight of the bird over a greater area and thus making it less likely to break through the snow crust. White coloring is another aid to winter survival, helping bird and background blend together.

In winter the willow ptarmigan turns completely white except for black on its tail and the color of its bill and its eyes, which do not change.

Like most other species of ptarmigan, the willow molts almost constantly. In the winter it is completely white except for its black tail, eyes and bill. As the snow begins to melt, this bird begins to lose some of its white feathers and brown ones come in. It then looks like the landscape about it—brown earth with patches of snow. In the summer the males have reddish-brown breasts and heads and look like the European red grouse. The females are mottled brown and white. With the beginning of winter and the first snows the ptarmigan molt again and eventually become white birds.

Even the toes of ptarmigan have feathers on them. Their feet are more heavily feathered in the winter than in the summer, making it easier for them to walk on top of the snow.

When the mating season arrives in the spring, the male willow ptarmigan fights other males and struts about to impress the female. The female builds a nest on the ground often near a small bush. Usually these birds nest in mountain areas or on the tundra, but on some Alaskan islands they nest on beaches. The nest is a depression in the ground lined with grasses.

The female lays from seven to ten eggs with bright red markings on them. A few hours after the eggs have been laid these markings have changed to dark brown. The female does not begin incubating the eggs until she has laid the last one.

The male stays near the nest and attempts to guard it from intruders. When the chicks hatch, he helps care for them.

The babies are covered with yellow, black, and brown down when they come out of the shell. They are capable of running to hide about an hour after they hatch, and can fly before they are two weeks old.

The family travels about feeding on leaves, fruit and insects. If they are disturbed, one of the adult birds will suddenly take flight, the young will seem to explode into the air and the other adult will be the last one to leave the ground. When they are in the air it is possible to see the white patch in the adult birds' wings.

They often come down to valleys and foothills during the winter, where they eat willow buds and leaves of other plants.

The willow ptarmigan is a very important source of food to many Eskimos and Indians, especially those who live far from any trading center. One Alaskan Indian name for the birds means "with an eye like a salmon berry"; another Indian name means "having a comb on the head." The latter refers to the birds' small, red comb.

The willow ptarmigan live not only in northern North America but also in the far northern countries of Europe and Asia.

Another ptarmigan which looks very much like the willow, but is two to four inches smaller, is the rock ptarmigan. It also lives in the mountains or on the tundra of northern countries around the world. In addition there are small isolated groups of these birds which live above the timberline in the European Alps, and in the mountains of Asia.

The rock ptarmigan also molts twice a year, and as a result always matches the ground where it spends most of its time. In the wintertime the males have small black lines from their beaks to and beyond their eyes. This is the only difference between their winter plumage and that of the willow ptarmigan.

During the spring and fall, when the ptarmigan is just losing or gaining its white winter plumage, it goes through a mottled patchwork stage, which, far from being imperfect, is better camouflage for those seasons than would be all-brown or all-white.

The rock ptarmigan often dig holes in the snow and roost in them in order to keep warm. They also scratch down in the snow with their feathered feet to get willow and birch buds. In the tundra regions these trees are dwarfed so they are really like bushes and are easy for the ptarmigan to reach.

The remaining species of ptarmigan, the white-tailed, is seldom seen except by mountain climbers. It lives almost at the snow line in mountains of Alaska and Canada and in the high Rockies of the United States.

The number of ptarmigan fluctuates throughout a ten-year cycle. At the beginning of the cycle the birds are very numerous, becoming fewer in numbers each year until at the end of the cycle they are scarce. Then, in a sudden population explosion, they become numerous again. No one knows the reasons for these fluctuations. The cycles do not seem to be related to the food supply available to the birds. The people who depend on the ptarmigan for part of their food supply, as well as arctic animal predators, are affected when ptarmigan are scarce.

147

ELEGANT ONES

What is beauty or grace or elegance in the natural world? Are they qualities unevenly distributed throughout creation or does man merely perceive them unevenly? Is the swan more beautiful than the swallow, the penguin more elegant than the porpoise, the flamingo more graceful than the fox?

We may find the answer to such questions in the way we use the word "natural." A "natural athlete" is one who performs with evident ease and grace. A "natural beauty" is one unaided by artifices of any kind. A "natural manner" is one that is easy and unstrained. Natural, in short, means to us that which is appropriate and believable. Unnatural means the opposite. An unnatural walk is ungainly, an unnatural position uncomfortable, an unnatural smile unconvincing.

And this is the answer to what we regard as grace and elegance and beauty in the natural world.

THE SWANS

SWANS play a prominent part in the folklore of Europe—the dying swan is supposed to sing a final song of indescribable beauty; the seven princes turned into swans by an enchantress, finally rescued by their devoted sister Lisa; the enchanted maidens who are swans in the famous Russian ballet *Swan Lake.* One of the best-known stories of all is Hans Christian Andersen's *Ugly Duckling* in which a cygnet, a baby swan, raised with ducks, eventually becomes a beautiful adult swan.

The mute swans of England have been considered royal birds, the property of the Crown, since 1482. Private owners can raise and keep these swans only when they obtain a royal license to do so.

There are only eight kinds of swans in the world. Six of them live in the northern hemisphere. The whooper, mute, Jankowski's and Bewick's swans live in Europe and Asia; the trumpeter and whistling swans live in North America. All six of these swans are large white birds.

148

The elegant black swan of Australia was cause for amazement when first seen by people from Europe, which has no species of swan remotely like it.

The whistling swans of North America spend the summer nesting north of the Arctic Circle, where they arrive about the first of May. There the pairs raise from one to five young cygnets.

They leave their breeding grounds in the fall and spend the winter in California and along the Chesapeake Bay in the eastern part of the United States. They have been these big wild swans in western and middle-western parts of the United States, but their nesting grounds were replaced by farms. The swans were also hunted almost to the point of extinction. Now they are legally protected and there are small colonies in Yellowstone National Park and in Red Rocks Refuge as well as in sanctuaries in Canada and Alaska. The trumpeters

protected by law since 1918 and it is illegal to hunt them. They are somewhat smaller than the mute swans, an adult measuring about three and a half feet in length, and have black bills and feet.

Trumpeter swans, the only other native North American species, are the largest swans, being almost five and a half feet long and weighing about twenty-five pounds. Like the whistling swans, they have black bills and feet. However, their nesting range extends farther south, down as far as Wyoming and Montana.

At one time there were large numbers of tend to stay in these areas all year rather than migrate for the winter months. They have a loud, musical, trumpeting call.

The two swans which live in the southern hemisphere are unique because they have black feathers. The one which lives in South America is the black-necked swan. It lives all the way south from Brazil to the Falkland Islands. Only its neck is black; the rest of its body is covered with conventional white feathers like the northern species. It averages about three and a half feet in length. It is often seen in zoos, but in zoos in the northern hemisphere these swans have trouble trying to raise young. Since the seasons are opposite to those of their home, they lay their eggs at the beginning of winter.

The other southern hemisphere swan is the black swan of Australia. The Dutch sailors who first saw this swan when they were exploring the Australian coast in 1697 could hardly believe their eyes. They took black

gust to December—spring and summer in the southern hemisphere. If there is a drought they do not nest.

The young birds' first plumage consists of gray feathers; only when they are adults do they have black feathers.

Adults have unusual curled feathers on their backs as well as white flight feathers, or primaries, in their wings. The white

Originally found only in Australia and Tasmania, the black swan has been introduced into New Zealand, where it is domesticated on ponds in parks. There are now great flocks living there in a wild state.

swans back with them to Batavia in the Dutch East Indies and later to Europe. However, these unusual swans did not become really popular in Europe until Josephine, the wife of Napoleon, acquired some for the royal parks.

In their native land the black swans spend the winter on salt water in coastal areas. In the spring they migrate to the southern part of the continent to nest on fresh water lakes. Like other swans, they build a bulky nest on islands or in shallow water. They lay from four to seven greenish-white eggs. The nesting period is from Au-

feathers show only when the birds fly. They have red beaks and red eyes.

The black swans were killed by the native Australians and by the early settlers. Now they are protected by law and their only enemies, especially during the nesting season, are the foxes, which the settlers introduced to the country, and water rats.

Black swans are shown on the armorial standard of Western Australia and have been pictured on Australian stamps. The river at Perth, where the black swans were first seen by the Dutch, is named Swan River.

THE EMUS AND CASSOWARIES

EMUS are one of the two very large flightless birds which can still be seen in the wild in Australia. They live on inland plains.

Emus have brownish-gray feathers which form a heavy coat over their bodies. Only two patches of bare blue skin on their necks and their heavy legs are not feathered. They are as tall as a man, adults reaching five and a half feet in height, and weigh as much as one hundred and twenty pounds. They are the second largest birds in the world; only the ostriches of Africa are larger.

During most of the year emus travel about in small flocks in grassland regions of Australia. They eat plants, fruits, insects and small animals.

When nesting time comes in February and March they pair off. Each pair builds a nest on the ground out of grasses and leaves and the female lays from seven to ten eggs. The eggs are big—each may be five and a half inches long and weigh as much as a pound and a half. Only the father sits on the eggs; he has to incubate them for about two months. When the young emus finally hatch, the father alone takes care of them.

Baby emus do not look like their parents; they have striped yellow and brown down at first. This probably helps protect them from predators, because it is very difficult to see them in their native habitat. It takes about two years before young emus become adult birds and raise families of their own.

Emus are rather gentle birds. They are curious about any strange creature which appears and will sometimes come up to men and stare with large pale-brown eyes.

The early settlers in Australia killed emus for food and also ate their eggs. Even now the farmers and emus are not on good terms. The big birds eat the farmer's crops and crash through the fences which have been built to keep them out of cultivated fields. At one time the men who were trying to raise wheat in western Australia asked the government for help against emus, and a small number of soldiers was sent out to shoot the birds. Emus can run very rapidly and can also swim well, and the

Native to the inland plains of Australia, the emu is a large and flightless bird, standing five and a half feet in height when full grown, and covered with long shaggy feathers. It has small wings evolved to an apparently useless form.

soldiers were unable to kill very many of them on the birds' home ground, so the "Emu War" was a failure. Since then a fence five hundred miles long, supposed to be secure against emus, has been put up in the interior region of the country and it is constantly checked to make sure that emus do not break through it.

Fortunately Australians, like Americans, are now beginning to value the original wildlife of their country. There are plans for setting up wildlife sanctuaries where emus as well as other rare Australian animals can live in peace.

Emus do well in captivity—as a matter of fact they do so well in some zoos that the flocks have grown to greater numbers than the zoos have room for.

According to scientists who have studied fossil remains, other species of emus lived in the Australia-Tasmania area as long ago as a hundred thousand years. Now there is only one species left.

The other big flightless bird of Australia is the cassowary. There are also other species of cassowaries found in New Guinea and on surrounding islands. The Australian cassowary lives in forests in the northeastern part of the continent.

Unlike the emus, adult cassowaries are not friendly. They strike out with their powerful clawed feet and are capable of killing a man. In zoos they often fight with each other, and even males and females have to be kept in separate pens. In spite of this bird's aggressiveness, some of the primitive peoples of New Guinea keep captive cassowaries and use their feathers as money.

Cassowaries have a strange bony covering, which looks like a helmet, on their heads. The exact purpose of this is not known, but scientists think it may protect

153

the bird's head as it travels through the thick underbrush of its forest home.

The skin of cassowaries' heads and upper neck is featherless and is bright red and blue. Some species have long folds of skin, called wattles, which hang down from their necks. Other than serving as decoration, these strange wattles seem to have no particular function.

Practically everything about the emu is large, from its stride, which carries it at speeds up to an estimated thirty miles an hour, to its eggs, which, laid seven or more in a clutch, average over five inches in length and one and a half pounds in weight.

The plumage of adult cassowaries is black and quite heavy. The birds stand about five feet tall; the female is somewhat larger than the male.

Shy birds seldom seen in their native forests, they can run at rapid speeds through the forest undercover and are also excellent swimmers. They eat fruits, insects and small animals. Their calls are a combination of grunts and bellows.

At nesting time the pairs build large nests of leaves on the ground and each female lays from three to six dark-green eggs. Then she departs and the male takes over, sitting on the nest until the young birds hatch. At first the young are striped, but their later feathers are brown and eventually, when they are adults, they have black feathers.

Other big flightless ground birds still found in the world today are the ostriches of Africa and the rheas of South America.

154

THE PENGUINS

PENGUINS fly in the water rather than above the water. Their wings have become almost like flippers, useless for flying but fine for propelling the birds through the water at speeds up to twenty-five miles an hour. Their webbed feet are used as rudders.

Except for the breeding and nesting seasons, penguins spend most of their lives at sea, swimming about with just their heads showing. They eat squids and fish in the water and drink the salty water of the sea. Even the penguins' eyes are adapted for seeing in the water; on land the birds act as if they were near-sighted.

Penguins are found only in the southern hemisphere. Two of seventeen species nest in the Antarctic. The other fifteen species nest on coastal islands of South America, New Zealand, Australia, and southern Africa.

Color variations among the species are generally found in head feathers, eyes, bills and feet. Except for these areas, most penguins are black and white, although the patterns vary among the species.

The emperor penguin is the largest of all species. The adults stand almost four feet tall and weigh about seventy-five pounds. In March, autumn below the equator, the emperor penguins begin arriving at their ancestral nesting grounds in the Antarctic. They come in groups, fat and sleek from months of feeding at sea. Often they make five-foot-high leaps out of the water onto

the ice, landing on their feet. Then they begin their waddling walk inland to the nesting area. Their legs are placed so far back on their bodies, that, out of water, the

One of the distinguishing features of the gray-blue gentoo penguin is the white band that arcs over its head above the brow. This elegantly attired bird is a native of the southern hemisphere, living near the South Shetlands and other small islands.

upright birds trudge along at a slow pace. Sometimes, especially if they are pursued, they toboggan over the snow and ice on their bellies. Then they can make rapid progress.

Penguins often mate for long periods, if not for life. When they arrive at the nesting grounds, only those breeding for the first time or those finding themselves without mates have to find new mates.

The single white egg is laid by the female in May. Then a long ordeal begins for the male emperor penguin because he alone is responsible for hatching it. The female heads back to sea to feed.

No place in the world is colder than the Antarctic in winter. Not only are there terrible winds, but the temperature drops far below zero Fahrenheit.

The male penguin has to balance the egg on his feet, covering it with a flap of skin and feathers on his lower abdomen; if it touches the ground or is exposed to the air for even a short time it freezes. Not all members of the penguin colony have eggs, but all would like to have one to hatch. If an egg is dropped by a parent, it may be broken by other penguins attempting to get it for themselves.

During storms the males that are incubating gather in groups for greater warmth, hopping about carefully, each with an egg balanced on its feet.

The eggs hatch in about two months and within a few days the mother penguins arrive to take charge of the babies. The fathers then go off to sea to break their long fast. They have not eaten since they came to the nesting grounds in March, and have lost at least one-third of their weight. They return within the month to help take care of the young.

Young emperor penguins are covered with grayish down. They spend the first days of their lives on the feet of their parents; they feed by sticking their heads into their parents' gullets to get regurgitated food. If any young birds are accidentally left on the ground by their parents, there are many non-breeding birds ready to take care of them.

Within four or five months from the time the young hatch, they have lost their down and acquired their feathers. In the meantime the colony has begun to break up and move back to the sea. The first birds to go are those which do not have young. The emperors move off from Antarctica in small orderly groups, usually on ice flows, as the ice breaks up in the summer. The young, in brown plumage, are among the last to leave. About two years later they will have adult breeding plumage and will return to the Antarctic continent. There they will breed near the place where they were hatched.

About the time the first migrant emperors are leaving the Antarctic, the Adelie penguins are arriving in flocks for their nesting season. They are much smaller than the emperors, being only about one and a half feet tall.

The Adelies nest in windswept areas where there is little snow. Nests are built of pebbles, the only material available in this region. Part of their courtship ritual is the presentation of pebbles to a potential partner. Male and female penguins look alike and apparently even they cannot

The male and female gentoo penguins alternate in the incubation of the eggs and in care of the young. It takes about thirty-three days for the two eggs to hatch.

readily tell the difference between the sexes.

An Adelie male goes courting with a pebble in his beak. If he presents it to an unresponsive female, or one already mated, she pays no attention to him. If he offers it to a male, he has a fight on his hands. But if he offers it to an unmated and willing female, she accepts it. From then on it is the male's job to get pebbles, preferably round ones, to complete the nest. He spends much of his time trying to steal these from neighboring nests.

Eggs appear in the nests in November and hatch in about a month. The parents sometimes eat snow during this mating and incubation period, but otherwise they fast. Adelies nest in large colonies of from 100,000 to almost 500,000 birds.

The king penguin looks very much like the emperor penguin but is smaller and has yellowish feathers on its breast. The king penguin stands about three feet tall and breeds in the Falklands and other sub- antarctic islands. Like the emperor, the king penguins hold the precious eggs on their feet.

The gentoo penguin nests in the Falklands and on small islands off the tip of South America. It is a shy bird, but fairly common, and was called Johnny Penguin by the seal hunters. It is the only penguin which has a white mark on its head.

The gentoo penguin spends the four or five winter months at sea. In spring it moves inland to nest.

Its chief enemies are those of most penguins, the leopard seal and the skuas. The leopard seals catch adult penguins in the water. Skuas, large birds of the southern hemisphere, eat the unattended eggs and young of the penguins.

The gentoo penguin was called Johnny Penguin by the seal hunters who, with the egg-stealing skuas, were the greatest threat to their safety. The penguin is a gregarious bird, especially at breeding time, when it moves inland in enormous numbers.

THE GIRAFFES

JULIUS CAESAR arranged to have a giraffe brought to Rome in 46 B.C. The Romans thought this strange-looking animal had a camel for a mother and a leopard for a father. Of course its parents were giraffes.

Giraffes live only in Africa, south of the Sahara Desert. They are found in dry plains areas where they can travel about easily. It is impossible for them to walk in mud and they cannot swim. On the plains they move freely and can run at speeds of thirty miles an hour.

They usually travel in small herds consisting of a male and several females with their young. Baby giraffes are five and a half feet high at birth. They nurse for about nine months, after which time they are tall enough to reach and eat leaves of trees.

Giraffes are vegetarians. Their favorite food is leaves and branches of the acacia trees which are plentiful on the African plains. Giraffes get moisture from leaves and can go for several weeks without drinking water. If water is available, though, they will drink. In order to get their heads down to the water they have to spread their front legs wide apart. They are very vulnerable to attack by lions when they are in this position. Lions are the only animals other than men that will kill a giraffe.

Giraffes are the tallest of all the animals, the males often reaching a height of eighteen or nineteen feet. It would be possible for a man of average height to stand upright between a giraffe's front legs. The neck of a giraffe may be five to six feet long; although there are no more vertebrae in it than in the neck of a cow—the vertebrae are just longer. The giraffe can extend its tongue out as far as eighteen inches from its mouth, which

enables it to reach leaves of trees with ease.

There are several kinds of giraffes. Each has a different color pattern and a different number of small horns on their heads. The reticulated giraffe of eastern Africa, for example, has large brown spots separated by narrow white lines. The blotched giraffe has paler spots separated by larger whitish lines. They come from different sections of Africa.

Deep in the Congo jungle lives a small relative of the giraffe, the okapi. This animal was unknown to scientists until the beginning of this century. It is much smaller than the giraffe and has a short neck. Its fur is almost brownish purple and there are white stripes on its legs.

Some fifteen million years ago giraffes which looked much like okapis lived in Asia as well as in Africa.

Even the antelope with its legendary swiftness is no match for the cheetah, the "hunting leopard."

THE CHEETAHS

CHEETAHS are the fastest runners in the animal kingdom. Within two seconds after starting they can reach speeds of forty miles an hour and can even reach sixty for a few hundred yards. They cannot keep up such speeds, however, and must catch their prey soon after beginning the run.

At one time cheetahs lived in India and the rulers of Indian states often had a pair of these "hunting leopards" trained to bring down gazelles and other antelopes. The cheetahs were taken to the hunt on a cart. Their heads were hooded. When an antelope was sighted, the cheetahs' heads were uncovered, and they were released. The cats would creep up on the game, and then with a sudden burst of speed, would overtake the frantic antelope and kill it.

Cheetahs are now rare in Asia. They are found mainly in Africa, where they are also becoming rare. As with other game animals, they have been over-hunted.

These unusual cats weigh about one hundred pounds and, including their long tails, measure about seven feet in length. They have long thin legs and the claws on their feet cannot be retracted into sheaths.

In the wild they often hunt during the day unlike other members of the cat family which hunt mainly at night. In open country they sometimes watch for their prey from small hills. A pair usually hunt together.

Cheetahs are tan or yellowish with black spots. Baby cheetahs are gray and do not have spots.

THE FLAMINGOS

A FEW years ago ornithologists estimated that there were about six million flamingos in the world. This included all the flamingos in Europe, Asia and Africa, as well as those of the Americas. Unfortunately these beautiful and unusual birds are decreasing in number although in many areas they are now protected by law.

The most colorful flamingos are those of the New World, especially the American flamingo which lives in the Caribbean and parts of South America. The adult American flamingos have pinkish-red feathers instead of the pinkish-white feathers of the birds living in the Old World.

Flamingos have a five-foot wingspread and stand about five feet tall. They have very long legs and necks, and fly with them outstretched. They are usually seen feeding or flying in fairly large groups. On their colonial breeding grounds the flock may number as many as twenty thousand birds.

The beak of a flamingo is very different from that of any other bird. The top part of it is bent down and almost looks as if it had been broken. When the flamingo feeds, it lowers its head so its bill is upside down on the shallow bottom of the salty mud flat. Then it scoops up mud, algae, and small shrimp. The bird has special filters on its beak and bristles in its mouth so it can get rid of any shells or other inedible objects.

Flamingos live on salt flats in almost desert-like regions where few other crea-

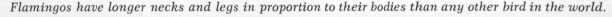

Flamingos have longer necks and legs in proportion to their bodies than any other bird in the world.

tures can live. Those that nest inland do so on shallow salt-water lakes like those in Kenya in Africa. One advantage of such areas is that there are almost no predators, and since these birds nest on the ground their eggs and young are therefore safe from other animals. However, nesting areas may be flooded or become too dry. Then a whole season may pass without any young flamingos being raised. Flamingos may also be frightened from their nesting areas by low-flying aircraft, and desert their nest for that season.

The American flamingos usually arrive at their nesting places in the Caribbean in February. They often come by night in small flocks until there are several thousand of them on one small island. They soon begin their displays. Long lines of females weave back and forth across the salt flats. The males stand about in small groups occasionally flicking their wings and pecking at one another. The air is filled with the sound of constant gabbling. Finally pairs are formed and cone-like nests of mud are built.

The female lays a single white egg in the nest. Both the parents take turns sitting on it for about a month. They usually exchange places in the morning and in the evening, giving each other a chance to feed.

When the young bird hatches, it is covered with white down which is later replaced by gray down. It stays in the nest for several days and then joins a flock of other young flamingos its own age. The young bird then may be fed by any adult bird, and not just by its own parents. When they first hatch the babies' beaks are not curved, but by the time they are six weeks old they have the same type of curved beaks as their parents.

By the time they are two and a half months old the young flamingos have developed their first brownish-white feathers and are able to fly. Flocks begin leaving the nesting grounds for the wintering grounds on other Caribbean islands and in South America. Not until they are four years old do the young birds acquire adult plumage and return to their ancestral nesting grounds to breed.

There are three other species of flamingos found in South America—the Chilean, the Andean, and the James's. They differ in color of feathers, bills and legs. The Andean and James's flamingos breed on salt water lakes high in the Andes. For a long time it was thought that the James's flamingo was extinct, but in 1957 ornithologists discovered some of these birds in a mountain lake in Bolivia. Two other ornithological expeditions were made to lakes in this region, and nesting flocks of James's flamingos were found. A few of these rare birds were captured and taken to the Bronx Zoo in New York City in 1960.

The flamingos found in Europe, Asia and Africa are white with light pink wings. Their nesting colonies are in Spain and France as well as in the Near East, India and Africa. The birds which nest in Europe spend the winters in Africa.

Flamingos have been in existence in the world for a long time. Fossil remains date back about forty million years. Some five thousand years ago a Neolithic artist painted the picture of one on the wall of a cave in Spain. This painting can still be seen today.

Flamingos prefer salt or brackish waters, not only getting most of their food from the muddy bottoms of such places, for which their long necks and stilt-like legs serve them very well, but also for building their nests and raising their chicks.

THE WHITE STORKS

SINCE the Middle Ages people of Central Europe have regarded the white storks as bringers of good luck to men. It is not known how such a legend arose but it has protected the storks. Perhaps it came about because the return of the storks meant that spring had come. In the 1700's watchmen in European towns announced the first sight of storks in the spring with a trumpet call.

The white storks appear to like the company of men. Originally they nested in tall trees but have given this up in favor of nesting on rooftops of churches and houses. And, because they are supposed to bring good luck, people in Central Europe have welcomed them, going so far as to put up wheels and platforms so the storks can easily find a place to build their heavy, bulky nests.

Even in the United States, where the white storks exist only in zoos, the big birds are often pictured as a symbol of maternity, probably a carry-over from some obscure European tradition.

Early in the spring the white storks which winter in Africa begin flocking in large groups. They circle high in the sky soaring on updrafts of warm air. Then, still in large groups, they take off for their ancestral nesting grounds in Europe, arriving in April or May. Some flocks go through Spain; some go through the Near East and the Balkans, and a few go across the Mediterranean and through Italy.

The males usually arrive at the nesting sites first, followed soon after by the females. Storks are thought to mate for life, but, if a partner fails to show up within a reasonable time, the stork that arrived first will take a new mate. They often use the same nest for several years, adding new material to it each year. The male hunts for sticks; the female fits them into the nest. Adult white storks, like all other storks, are voiceless, so their courtship displays consist of circular flights and bill clacking. They also have a peculiar display in which they throw their heads backward onto their backs, which makes them look as if they had broken necks. This particular display continues throughout their nesting period.

Eventually the female lays three to five white eggs which both parents take turns incubating for a month. When the babies finally hatch they are fed with insects, frogs, mice, and other small animals which the parents have picked up in lakes, marshes and fields near the nesting site.

The young storks remain in the nest for about two months. Then they are able to fly and can join their mother and father in hunting for food. In the fall when the flocks begin to migrate south, the parents usually leave before the young. The young birds apparently know instinctively where and by what route to fly south for the winter. They return to a place near where they were hatched when they are ready to nest.

White storks are large handsome white birds with black wing tips. They may stand as high as four feet. They have red feet and long straight red bills. At one time they were found in Asia as far east as China and Japan, but their numbers are decreasing. Only in Central Europe are they still a relatively common bird.

The European white stork is a large and handsome bird, with red feet, a red bill, and black on its wings. It may reach four feet in height.

THE PELICANS

PELICANS are often seen flying in flocks in a V shape or line formation. Sometimes, depending on the wind, they fly close to the water with their long wings nearly touching the waves. At other times they can be seen circling very high in the sky.

Pelicans are large birds. The average white pelican of North America weighs from ten to seventeen pounds when it is full grown. It is from four to five feet long and has a wingspan of eight or nine feet. Brown pelicans are smaller, usually weighing about eight pounds, and having a wingspan of seven and a half feet.

These birds are found almost everywhere in warm and temperate regions. The brown and the white pelicans are the only species in the Americas. In Europe, Africa, southern Asia, and Australia there are six species. Pelicans have existed in the world for a very long time. Fossil remains date back to between thirty or forty million years ago.

All pelicans have a throat, or gular, pouch which can be extended when they are feeding. The gular pouch of the American white pelican can hold as much as three gallons. This pelican fishes from the surface of the water; the brown pelican dives into the water for its food.

The white pelicans sometimes have a community fishing arrangement. They gather in a semi-circle on the surface of shallow water and with noisy splashings drive the fish in towards shore. Then, almost in unison, they gather the fish into their voluminous pouches. Pelicans for the most part eat "trash fish," that is, fish which are not valuable to the commercial fisherman.

In March and April the white pelicans of North America begin their long migration from the Gulf Coast to their inland breeding areas. Over mountains and deserts they fly, to islands in fresh water lakes in Utah, Wyoming, and western Canada. A few nest in coastal areas, but most of the seven major breeding areas of white pelicans in North America are in fresh water.

They nest in colonies of from a few birds to several hundred pairs, depending on the local food supply. They may lay their chalky white eggs on the ground or in mounds of earth from eight to twelve inches high.

Baby pelicans are naked when they come out of the eggs, but within a week they are covered with white down. Their first feathers are gray.

When the young are about four weeks old they leave their nest and gather into groups with other young pelicans.

From the time of hatching until the young are ready to feed on their own, the parents have had to supply each one with about one hundred and fifty pounds of fish. In order to do this the parent birds may have had to fly as far as one hundred miles a day to get food.

In September and October the white pelicans fly south to winter along the Gulf Coast.

The brown pelicans follow much the same breeding pattern, but they are coastal birds and are seldom seen inland.

The white pelican: a persistent fisherman with a dip net for a mouth and an appetite to match it.

THE WILD OXEN

It is hard to imagine a world without the large herds of domestic cattle found in almost every country. Men use these animals in many important ways—their milk and meat provide people with a valuable source of protein. Cattle hides are used extensively for leather goods.

Modern breeds of cattle were developed from wild oxen. They were possibly first domesticated as beasts of burden, but the Egyptians were milking their cattle as long as five thousand years ago. Cattle were also sacrificed in early religious rites.

The ancestor of many domestic breeds of cattle was the huge *Bos primigenius* of Europe and North Africa. They were large —bulls stood seven feet tall at the shoulders —and lived in wild herds. Primitive man drew pictures of them in caves in southern France and these pictures can still be seen today. The last herd of these wild cattle, found in Eastern Europe, apparently died out in the sixteenth century.

At Chillingham Park in England there is a herd of "wild cattle" which are supposed to be direct descendants of the *Bos primigenius*. Actually these cattle are probably domestic cattle that were permitted to return to the wild several centuries ago.

The humped cattle of India, also thought to be descended from the *Bos primigenius,* are important to the people of Asia. Certain bulls of this breed are regarded as sacred and are permitted to walk about the towns freely.

Asians have also domesticated the yak and the water buffalo, two other members of the Bovidae family. In the wild the water buffalo is regarded as one of the most dangerous game animals.

Wild oxen were the ancestors of the modern breeds of domestic cattle. Bos primigenius, as one ancient species is called, stood seven feet high at the shoulders and lived in wild herds. The horns of a cow are true horns and are not shed during the cow's life.

THE CARIAMAS

THERE are only two species of cariamas found in the world today and both live in South America. But the cariamas are related to giant flightless birds which walked about the South American continent more than forty million years ago. The largest of these ancient carnivorous birds, Phororhacos, stood five feet tall and had a bill fifteen inches long. Cariamas are also distantly related to *Diatryma*, the huge seven-foot-tall bird which lived in North America during the Eocene Period. Scientists have been able to determine that these birds were related by studying their fossil remains and comparing their various body structures with those of present-day cariamas.

One species of cariama is called the crested; the other is called Burmeister's. The crested cariama lives on the grasslands of western Brazil and northern Argentina. It spends most of its time walking on the ground and runs rapidly, instead of flying to escape from its enemies. At night it roosts in low trees. It generally travels with one other cariama or with a small flock. It eats fruit, berries, insects, lizards and snakes. Sometimes farmers capture young cariamas and put them with their chickens in order to keep their farmyards free of snakes.

Cariamas begin mating in the spring and the males strut, giving strange dog-like yelping calls in an effort to impress the females. The crested cariamas nest on the ground.

The females lay two brown-spotted eggs. The parents take turns incubating the eggs which hatch in about three and a half weeks. The young are covered with down when they emerge from the egg.

Like the crested cariama, the Burmeister's cariama has long legs and grayish-brown feathers but it is slightly smaller. It lives in brushland areas instead of open grasslands, and builds its nest in low trees.

Cariamas are said to have the odd habit of giving loud calls if they sense danger from afar only to become perfectly silent when danger is near. At the last minute they put their heads down and swiftly run away. They can fly, but not as well as most birds.

Cariamas are classified as belonging to the order Gruiformes, which includes the cranes, rails, and bustards. Some ornithologists think that this very old order of birds, which now contains only twelve families, is on its way out. Many species in it have recently become extinct or are, like the whooping crane of North America, on the verge of extinction.

The cariamas resemble the bustards of Europe, Asia, Africa and Australia more closely than they do any other bird in the order. The bustards, like the cariamas, live on grassy plains and in brushland, and have brownish-gray feathers. The great bustard of Europe is about three and a half feet tall; the cariama stands about two feet tall.

INDEX

CREDITS

Photographs in this book were
taken by the following.

WILLIAM A. ANDERSON
DON ARLEN
LLOYD BEEBE
DICK BORDEN
DR. WALTER J. BRECKENRIDGE
WILLIAM AND MARY CARRICK
ARTHUR S. CARTER
JOEL E. COLMAN
JACK C. COUFFER
ROBERT H. CRANDALL
HERB AND LOIS CRISLER
MURL DEUSING
ROY EDWARD DISNEY
WARREN E. GARST
CLEVELAND P. GRANT
CONRAD HALL
FRAN WILLIAM HALL
AL HANSON
BERT HARWELL
CLAUDE JENDRUSCH
STUART V. JEWELL
N. PAUL KENWORTHY, JR.
TOM McHUGH
ELMA AND ALFRED MILOTTE
GEORGE MUSHBACH
TAD NICHOLS
WALTER PERKINS
OLIN SEWALL PETTINGILL, JR.
JAMES R. SIMON
HUGH AND MARY WILMAR